Lecture No
Behavioural !

CW00959563

Edited by

A.C.P. SIMS
MA MD FRCPsych
Professor of Psychiatry
University of Leeds

and

W.I. HUME
BSc PhD DCP
Lecturer in Clinical Psychology
University of Leeds

BLACKWELL SCIENTIFIC PUBLICATIONS
OXFORD LONDON EDINBURGH
BOSTON MELBOURNE

© 1984 by
Blackwell Scientific Publications
Editorial offices:
Osney Mead, Oxford, OX2 OEL
8 John Street, London, WC1N 2ES
9 Forrest Road, Edinburgh, EH1 2QH
52 Beacon Street, Boston
  Massachusetts 02108, USA
99 Barry Street, Carlton
  Victoria 3053, Australia

First published 1984

Set and printed in Hong Kong by
LP & Associates Ltd

DISTRIBUTIONS

USA
Blackwell Mosby Book Distributors
11830 Westline Industrial Drive
St. Louis, Missouri, 63141

Canada
Blackwell Mosby Book Distributors
120 Melford Drive, Scarborough
Ontario, M1B 2X4

Australia
Blackwell Scientific Book Distributors
31 Advantage Road, Highett
Victoria 3190

British Library
Cataloguing in Publication Data

Sims, A.C.P.
  Lecture notes on behavioural
  sciences.
  1. Human behavior
  I. Title   II. Hume, W.I.
  300   BF57
  ISBN 0-632-00967-5

Contents

Contributors

All contributors are members of the University of Leeds

Jan Aldridge-Smith   BA MSc *Lecturer in Psychology, Department of Psychiatry*

R.E.H. Ballard   MA PhD *Lecturer in Race Relations, Department of Psychology*

S.J. Baugh   MB ChB MRCPsych *Lecturer, Department of Psychiatry*

C.R. Brewin   BA MSc PhD *Lecturer in Psychology, Department of Psychiatry*

A.W.J. Butler   BA DipPsychother AAPSW MISW *Lecturer in Mental Health Social Work, Department of Psychiatry*

Isobel R. Card   MB ChB MRCP FRCPsych *Lecturer in Psychiatry, Department of Psychiatry*

A.R. Dabbs   BA DipPsychol *Senior Lecturer in Clinical Psychology, Department of Psychiatry*

W.I. Hume   BSc PhD DCP *Lecturer in Clinical Psychology, Department of Psychiatry*

R.H.S. Mindham   MD FRCP FRCPsych DCH *Nuffield Professor of Psychiatry, Department of Psychiatry*

A.C.P. Sims   MA MD FRCPsych *Professor of Psychiatry at St. James's Hospital, Department of Psychiatry*

R.P. Snaith   MD FRCPsych DCH *Senior Lecturer in Psychiatry, Department of Psychiatry*

Preface

'Behavioural Sciences' is a relatively new subject on the medical curriculum. The Royal Commission on Medical Education (Todd Report, 1968) stated, 'There can be no doubt that the teaching normally provided by British medical schools (in behavioural sciences) is in need of great improvement'. Perhaps the surprise to a moderately reflective layman is that this subject was never on the curriculum before. Generations of doctors were trained learning in detail about the anatomy, physiology and biochemistry of man, but not about the behaviour of man in society, or more particularly about the behaviour of patients and of doctors.

There are a number of texts on psychology for medical undergraduates written by psychologists, and on sociology written by sociologists. However, to our knowledge there is no other book that combines these two disciplines for medical students, and that links the basic science to its clinical application. *Lecture Notes on Behavioural Sciences* attempts to give basic information about the relevant scientific disciplines and to demonstrate how this is related to clinical practice. Almost all the chapters are written by practitioners of either medicine, clinical psychology or social work, and the aim throughout has been to produce a text that is both basic and applied. We hope the reader will be encouraged to explore in greater depth the many topics covered. To facilitate this, further basic reading is referred to after many chapters.

A.C.P. SIMS
W.I. HUME

CHAPTER 1

Introduction

What are behavioural sciences?

The undergraduate medical curriculum is extremely full and so some justification is necessary for introducing another subject, Behavioural Sciences, to add to the enormous amount that has to be learned. Because of the wholly appropriate emphasis in medical education on scientific and technological advances in diagnosis and in treatment, it has become necessary to redress the balance and to teach more about *human behaviour*, its *variability* and how it manifests itself in *social groupings*. The intention of this book is to reinforce the idea in a number of different ways that human beings, patients, are whole people and need to be treated as such. They are also members of families, citizens, and representatives of other distinctive groupings. It is important not to lose sight of the fact that human illness occurs in a wider context than just the doctor's surgery.

Behavioural sciences are concerned with the scientific study of human behaviour. They provide a useful framework for the appreciation of how a sick person behaves in a medical setting, in a similar way to the application of biochemistry and physiology in pathology. The difficulty for human behaviour is that its scientific study is less advanced than for example, physics, although we intuitively 'know' more about behaviour before we begin scientific investigation. In physics, we are satisfied, if for example, we can predict what all the atoms of a particular kind are likely to do; we are not concerned with the behaviour of individual atoms. With human beings, however, individual variation is all important, and science has to progress to a more refined level than simply predicting the behaviour that is common to all.

1

Behavioural sciences are concerned with the observation and explanation of human behaviour, either in single individuals or in groups. The academic subjects of *psychology* and *sociology* are the most important behavioural sciences for consideration in medical training. Psychology is the study of the nature, functions and phenomena of human behaviour. Sociology and *social anthropology* are the study of the origins, history, mechanisms and constitution of human cultures. Behavioural sciences are also significantly linked with *human ecology*, that is, the branch of knowledge which deals with the relations of human beings to their environment and the quantification of this relationship; and to a lesser extent *epidemiology*, which is the study of illnesses in defined populations.

Relevance to medicine

The relevance of behavioural sciences to medicine is demonstrated in *aetiology*; in the *presentation of illnesses*; in the *delivery of health care*; and in aspects of *psychological* and *social treatment*. Both psychological and social factors are relevant in causing illness and this is discussed at greater length in Chapters 18 and 19. As examples of such causation, emotional disturbances and problems with personal relationships can cause both overeating and also, on occasions, a refusal to eat (anorexia nervosa). Whatever the psychological causes that may or may not be important, cigarette smoking is undoubtedly human behaviour, and it is a form of behaviour that is associated with morbidity and mortality. Links between occupation, social class or race and certain illnesses may be seen as social factors in aetiology. There is here an obvious overlap with Community Medicine.

Illnesses manifest as specific behaviours occurring in individual patients. Disease is not like a universal chemical reaction occurring in a test-tube. Changes in behaviour are important in different illnesses and also in different conditions of the organism, for example, with ageing. Behaviour may be altered to a very marked extent in association with psychiatric illness, or with severe pain, or with various types of neurological impairment, for example multiple sclerosis. The patient's response to his illness and its treatment is a highly individual matter where both psychological and social factors are relevant; for instance, it is very important to consider the behavioural and human aspects of a man aged 43 with three children at school, a wife and a mortgage, who learns that he has cancer. It is important to consider not only the reaction of the patient but also of the whole family when a sick member requires dialysis at home for renal failure.

Behavioural and social aspects are very important in the way health care is given to a community. Psychology and sociology are both relevant in making health education effective, for example, using the information that less than 50% of doctors smoke in persuading others to change their smoking behaviour. Behavioural and emotional aspects should be taken into consideration when decisions are made as to whether treatment should be in hospital or at home for various conditions such as coronary thrombosis, terminal malignant disease or mild dementia.

Various examples are given in this book of social and psychological factors which make a contribution to treatment. Thus it is valuable for the doctor to improve his interviewing skills, and also to establish a relationship in which his patients trust him. It is also useful for him to gain some knowledge of how the relationship with a patient may be therapeutic in reducing unhelpful illness behaviour and encouraging healthy attitudes. Behavioural modification techniques are often useful in the treatment of various conditions sometimes far removed from their original applications in psychiatry. Changing the patient's environment may be valuable for the improvement of both mental and physical symptoms. The doctor may be in a position to facilitate social change if he is sufficiently interested and knowledgeable about the social factors relevant to his patient to help in this way. The importance of considering cultural and ethnic factors in both the presentation of disease and its treatment should be stressed.

Methods of studying behaviour

Methods of collecting information about a group of people include: observation, questionnaires and other such structured enquiries, and interviews. Various documentary sources may also be helpful, including official reports and statistics, records of institutions, for example, the day book from wards of a hospital, and case notes which are perhaps the most important documents concerning behaviour. Other national and local data such as census information or employment statistics may be useful in health research.

Observation of the patient is always of importance in clinical medicine. Physical examination is, of course, necessary, but physical and behavioural perculiarities may be observed in addition during interview. In patients where verbal behaviour is limited or absent, for example in mental handicap, or in young children, or stuporose patients, observation is of course all-important. Machines may give additional help for improving observation or recording it, and participant observation, for example the comments of ward nurses, may be extremely valuable.

Questionnaires completed by the respondent, or recording schedules which the interviewer fills in, may be used for investigating behaviour. There are a number of different types of instrument such as check lists, rating scales, self-rating scales, visual analogue scales, rankings, inventories, and grids; all of which may be used for assessing different aspects of behaviour, emotional experience and attitudes. Psychological tests which are objective and standardised measures of a sample of behaviour are frequently used for the measurement of intelligence or aspects of personality.

Psychophysiology is the quantification of biological events as they relate to psychological variables. Such techniques may be used to investigate supposed relationships between bodily functions and certain emotional states or types of behaviour. A frequent problem is that the physiological measurements are much more precise than the psychological or emotional measures. An example of such combined physical and psychological assessment might be the recording of pulse rate and skin resistance of a subject who is exposed to anxiety-provoking stimuli, such as being asked to imagine walking into the examination hall. Measures of mood, particularly anxiety, would be made at the same times as the physiological measurements.

Principles of measurement

Any measurement in any area of study, if it is to be useful, must be both reliable and valid.

Reliability describes the consistency of an individual's score on repeated testing provided that the property being tested has not changed. *Test–retest reliability* is the correlation between scores using the same test given to the same individual on two different occasions. *Alternate form reliability* is the correlation between two forms of the same test. *Split half reliability* describes the correlation between two halves of the same test. *Inter-rater reliability* reflects the correlation between scores achieved by two different testers. Thus, reliability measures error in the test itself, or in the administration of the test. Should the variable being measured change from one occasion of testing to the next, then the methods of assessing reliability by repeated testing are inappropriate.

Validity describes the ability of a test to measure what it is claimed to measure. Different aspects of validity are important. In *content validity*, one is concerned with whether the test covers a representative sample of the different types of behaviour being measured. *Predictive validity* is concerned with whether a subject's test score predicts behaviour in defined situations. *Construct validity* is concerned with whether the test assesses a theoretical construct, such as *intelligence*. Clearly, validity is to do with the performance of a test relative to some external criterion. A valid test of blood pressure can be constructed because there is an agreed criterion against which to judge it. This is not so with many psychological constructs such as *anxiety* or *intelligence* where there is no external standard.

Prevalence of a disease is the number of cases present in a unit of population at a given time (*point prevalence*), or during a given period (*period prevalence*). *Incidence* is the number of new cases appearing in a unit of population in a given period of time, most often 1 year. The *expectancy* is the likelihood that an individual will develop the disease during a given period. *Caseness* is the arbitrary operational definition of what will be accepted as presentation of a disease in a particular population, for example, a different definition of hypertension would be appropriate in a community survey as opposed to a hospital cardiology clinic.

A fundamental aspect in making progress in science is that after experiments are reported, other workers replicate the work to see if they obtain the same findings. Although such replication is common in academic psychology, it is usually quite rare in either studies of health and disease, or in sociology. It is important therefore to learn as much as one can about different variables and their effects by observing and measuring them in a number of different populations.

Diagnosis

Every profession must conceptualize the problems it is called upon to solve in such a way that the skills of that profession may be made

most effective. Diagnosis is just that; the patient's problem described in terms which allow the doctor to carry out appropriate
action. Diagnosis is therefore dependent on accurate observation,
and it carries important implications for both management and
prognosis.

When diagnosis is put in its social and psychological context it
should not be a single word, for example, 'tuberculosis', but much
more a *diagnostic formulation* that describes a problem in biochemical, pathological, psychological and social terms, for
example: 'bacteriologically-proven tuberculosis in a man with
cirrhosis of the liver secondary to chronic alcoholism associated
with destitution, and living in lodging houses over the last several
years'.

Diagnosis is equally essential as an element of medical practice
whether it be in acute medicine or surgery, general practice or
psychiatry. Rational treatment with the expectation of benefit to
the patient is quite impossible without rational diagnosis.

Concepts of illness and health

This is discussed in more detail in Chapter 20. Health and disease,
being healthy or having an illness, affects the psychological state of
the individual and his social status and role. Illness is not seen as
being a neutral event but it is given the value judgement of being
definitely bad. Loss of function, the presence of pain and other
symptoms, the presence of deformity are usually considered by the
person himself and those around him to be of negative value and to
detract from him as a person.

Illness can be used to explain circumstances. For a person to be
described as 'ill' denotes a lack of personal responsibility, and may
be used as an excuse for defaulting in areas of life which are in fact
unconnected: "How could I be expected to have written that essay,
I had 'flu."

Illness also denotes a social role. An ill person takes a dependent
position in society and this is legitimized by the presence of illness.
In a sociological sense, the whole paraphernalia of medicine and its
ancillary professions may be seen as a means of establishing those
who are ill in such a role of sickness.

Health has proved extremely difficult to define. Many doctors
have a working definition that it is the *absence of disease*. Disease is
either seen as the presence of organic, histological, morbid patho-

logical or biochemical disorder or, alternatively, the presence of *biological disadvantage* as shown by *increased mortality* or *decreased fertility*. At a more elevated level, is the definition given by the World Health Organisation that 'health is a state of complete physical, mental and social well-being and not merely the absence of disease or infirmity'.

Scope of behavioural sciences

Information has accumulated over the last few years about how the individual *develops* psychosocially; that is, how people learn to behave the way they do. Human learning and development can be studied both from the individual (Chapters 2 and 4) and from the cultural standpoint (Chapter 3).

The single most fundamental difference between behavioural sciences, and the basic or natural sciences like chemistry or physics is the element of *individual variation*. As long as the vast majority of atoms behave in a certain way in a chemical reaction we do not usually enquire whether there are any deviants among the atomic population. However, in behavioural sciences, the very opposite is true; it is often study of the deviant which gives us most useful information about the conforming majority. Human beings differ in the functioning of their brains as much as in the shape of their faces (Chapter 7). Perception (Chapter 5), intelligence (Chapter 6), memory (Chapter 8), consciousness (Chapter 9), emotion (Chapter 10) and personality (Chapter 11) all show marked individual variation which require study. It is almost inconceivable that a doctor in training, who receives detailed information about the structure, composition and functioning of the human body, should not also be taught about these aspects of mankind; however, until quite recently this was the situation in fact.

Implicit within the differences between individuals is the effect human beings have upon each other and the way other's expectations affect the individual. Social differences, in terms of manifestation of social behaviour, are clearly important (Chapter 12). These differences reveal themselves especially in the way different families function (Chapter 14), and also in sex and gender role (Chapter 13).

It is the aim of this book to demonstrate how this emphasis upon the study of the individual and his interaction with society is relevant in medicine. The individual and social background to illness covers the effects of stress (Chapter 17) and personality (Chapter 16) and the presentation of illness; how behaviour and social circumstances may result in illness (Chapters 18 and 19); what is meant by *illness* and *illness behaviour* (Chapter 20); the special circumstances of old age (Chapter 22); the relationship between work and ill health (Chapter 21); and the variation of individual response to pain (Chapter 15).

Knowledge of behavioural sciences has implications for health care. This is true both in considering study of the relationships between the individual patient and doctor (Chapter 23), and also in looking at institutions, such as hospitals and the National Health Service, to see how they can most efficiently and humanely be therapeutic (Chapter 24 and 25). For health education to be effective, a grasp of psychological and social principles is essential (Chapter 29). The psychological sequelae of physical illness are important for the doctor to take into account (Chapter 26), and this is particularly so for the special circumstances of chronic illness and handicap, for acute loss and for bereavement (Chapters 27 and 28).

Further reading:

Moser C.A. & Kalton G. (1977) *Survey Methods in Social Investigation*, 2nd Edition. London, Heinemann.
Caplan A.L., Engelhardt H.T. & McCartney J.J. (1981) *Concepts of Health and Disease*, Reading, Massachussetts, Addison-Wesley.

CHAPTER 2

Development of Behaviour

This chapter is concerned with development in the early years of life. It is, however, important to set this in context and to remember that although the nature of development might change, the process continues throughout life. In adulthood the rate of development is much slower than in earlier years, but nevertheless biological, psychological and social changes are still taking place.

The newborn

In the last two decades much has been learned about infant behaviour. Due to improved techniques and methods of measurement we now know that even before birth not only can the fetus behave spontaneously but it can respond to stimulation and can show evidence of conditioned learning to sounds. At birth the neonate is a complex mixture of competence and incapacity. All vital organs are formed and functional. The baby can see, hear and smell, cry and move its limbs. It has a range of reflexive behaviours that can be observed to be elicited by specific stimuli. For example, the *rooting reflex*: a touch on the infant's cheek results in turning of the head, the mouth coming towards the stimulus, and sucking.

Contrary to popular belief newborn infants do not spend all their time sleeping, eating and crying. There is of course considerable variation between individuals but in the first week of life sleep averages 16 h 20 min, this reduces to 14 h 50 min by the 16th week. It does seem, therefore, that many infants are awake and free to devote their time to other things for about a third of each day. Even in the first week we now know that a baby's perceptual systems are geared for rudimentary social interaction. For example, the optimal distance at which a baby can see is about 20 cm, the distance at which they are usually placed for feeding or en-face social interaction; the range of sounds to which they are particularly sensitive is that of the human voice. It would seem that infants are geared to respond to particularly human characteristics. Indeed, from careful observation it is apparent that even the youngest baby attends to and interacts with its environment in a far from indiscriminate way. This means that the adult is not dealing with a 'psychological nonentity', nor with an inert, passive organism which must be stimulated into life. Rather, the task of the parent is to synchronize her or his behaviour with behaviour which is already organised. This behaviour can vary considerably as there are marked individual differences between infants and they bring their own demands and peculiarities to even the earliest encounters with others.

From the beginning the individuality of the child can exert a definite influence on how he or she is treated by others. For example, some babies are active and restless, others quiet; some like being held close and cuddled, others do not. The adult must adopt practices and behave to the infant in such a way that not only suits them but also suits the infant. Many people are able to do this, but when there is a conflict such as a quiet, cuddling mother with an active, restless, non-cuddler infant and the mother is not able to adapt her behaviour, the resultant mismatch can lead to the development of interaction difficulties. This does not mean that either the mother or the infant's behaviour is abnormal; just that they have different needs.

Developmental patterns

It is questionable whether there is a single developmental sequence for the emergence of physical characteristics, motor, language and social skills. The development of such separate skills and the approximate ages at which they appear are called *norms*. Norms are based on calculations that indicate average tendencies for a large number of children. Although norms are used to describe how most infants develop they are not intended to indicate the ideal since there is great variability between children. From birth children show individual differences in every measurable aspect of behaviour. Those differences shown at birth are determined genetically and by events during pregnancy, at birth and immediately afterwards. It is rare for there to be a single explanation for behaviour, many biological and environmental determinants work in concert.

For detailed descriptions of the general patterns of growth and change in the locomotor system, visuo-perceptual skills, social behaviour, language and communication the reader is referred to a text on development. Here we shall confine ourselves to noting three general principles that describe how growth is directed:

(1) cephalocaudal development,
(2) proximodistal development, and
(3) differentiation and integration.

Physical growth and motor abilities develop in two directions simultaneously. *Cephalocaudal development* refers to the fact that growth progresses from head to foot: a baby learns to hold up its head before it learns to sit, to sit before it can walk. *Proximodistal development* refers to growth progressing from the centre of the body to the periphery: control of the hand developing before control of its fingers. A third trend is *differentiation and integration*. Differentiation means that an infant's abilities become increasingly distinct and specific. Integration refers to the combining and integrating of a number of simple skills together to enable the performance of a more complex task. An example would be a child learning to drink from a cup.

Theories of development

Research in the area of child development has flourished in the past few decades. There is, however, no one theory which satisfactorily covers all aspects of human development. Three groups of theories of development are described:

(1) behaviour learning theories,
(2) stage theories, and
(3) psychodynamic theories.

Behaviour learning theories

Learning theories regard the human being as an organism that has largely developed through experience and learning. Behaviour is regarded as malleable, the role of the individual in his or her own development as more or less passive, and the development of behaviour as continuous over the lifespan. A particularly notable exponent of this position is Skinner, who has undertaken detailed investigation of the acquisition, retention and extinction of behaviour.

Stage theories

Stage theories regard people's behaviour as relatively changeable, their role in development as active and the development of behaviour as progressing by stages. Such theories argue that development is strongly cumulative but not continuous. Piaget's work, centering on the development of intelligence, is an example of such a view. Piaget proposes three major stages in intellectual development, arranged in a specific order, with the organisation of behaviour qualitatively different at each stage:

(1) sensorimotor period (birth–2 years),
(2) period of representational thought (2–11 years), and
(3) a formal operational period (12 + years).

During the sensorimotor period the infant is busy discovering the relationships between sensations and motor behaviour, differentiating self from objects and learning that objects continue to exist even though no longer visible (*object permanence*). The period of representational thought can be subdivided into preoperational and concrete operational periods. In the preoperational stage the child starts to record experiences symbolically. Play, language and thinking are integrated but may still be idiosyncratic and often dominated by perception. At about 7 or 8 years children enter the concrete operational period when they begin to understand new kinds of logical operations involving reversible transformations. They are now using abstract terms, but only in relation to concrete objects. By 11 or 12 young adolescents begin to develop a formal logic that shows general propositional thinking. They are able to reason in purely abstract terms; at this time they enter the formal operational period.

Psychodynamic theories

Psychodynamic theorists have concentrated on personality development. Their concern has been to understand and explain the development of both rational and irrational feelings and behaviour. Most psychodynamic theories discuss and analyze human development in terms of confrontations between the growing individual and the demands of the social world. They stress how the individual must accommodate to society whilst obtaining gratification for basic drives. Of the many psychodynamic theories, that based on the work of Freud was the earliest and is the best known.

It should be stressed that these three groups of theories do not necessarily conflict. They are often complementary, each focusing on and accounting for different aspects of the developmental process. Piaget's work, for example, has been influential in the study of cognitive development, the psychodynamic group of theories have contributed largely to the study of personality development and the methods of study of the behaviour—learning theorists have contributed not just in the area of learning, but to the study of many aspects of human behaviour.

Further reading:

Bower T.G.R. (1979) *Human Development*. Freeman, San Francisco.
McGurk H. (1975) *Growing and Changing*. Methuen, London.

CHAPTER 3

Significance of Culture

The nature of culture

All aspects of human activity are greatly influenced by culture.
Culture is best understood as being a matter of the values that
people use to give meaning and purpose to their lives, and the conventions that they employ to order their social interactions. Culture
consequently includes the language we speak, the way we organize
our families, the expectations we have about obligations inherent in
marriage, kinship and friendship, what we may or may not eat and
how we should eat it, dress, modesty, shame and dignity, what is
clean and what is dirty, how we should behave to signal illness.
Culture penetrates and gives order to every conceivable area of
human behaviour.

Culture is learned; it is neither instinctive nor hereditary. Human
cultures are also infinitely diverse. People everywhere use language
to communicate, live in small domestic groups, have ideas about
child rearing, cleanliness, manners, morality and so forth; but the
content of these conventions is immensely variable. Even within a
single society conventions vary from context to context, and
change over time. For example, even in the same climate nothing at
all may be worn on the beach, but such behaviour would not be
acceptable at a dinner party. In each sphere different conventions
apply, we are all quite skilled in making our behaviour appropriate
to its context, but when we find ourselves in situations where we do
not know what is expected of us we become conscious of culture as
an issue, and this is profoundly disturbing.

Culture is essentially about order, providing the foundations for
the complex work of relationships which humans create around
themselves. No activities, not even our most basic biological func-

14

tions, are left unordered. Take eating, for example. English children are taught to use knives, forks and spoons, and that to use their fingers is dirty except for eating bread or cake for which the left hand is used. Hindu rules are quite different. Food is invariably eaten with the fingers, though only of the right hand. Cutlery is regarded as dirty, because it has been in other people's mouths. Rules about eating, washing, defaecating and so forth are found everywhere, but differ widely in their content. Each system forms a more or less coherent whole, which makes good sense to those who use it.

Although there is no objective way in which cultures can be marked as superior or inferior, humans show a strong tendency towards making such ethnocentric judgments. Most people believe that their own conventional ways of doing things are not only convenient, but right. Hence they are likely to perceive other people's cultural styles as immoral, unacceptable or even pathological. Those who have been fortunate enough to acquire wealth and power are particularly likely to adopt such ideas of cultural superiority.

Culture and medical practice

How much does all this matter to doctors? Both they and their patients are people, and they interact with one another as social beings, not just as mobile biological systems. Doctors do not just encounter diseases as they are described in the textbooks, but they meet people who are ill, and illness, just like other forms of human behaviour, is culturally grounded. Hence in both diagnosing and treating their patients doctors must necessarily bring social skills to bear. However well qualified they may be in technical terms, the quality of service they can offer is impaired if they lack the requisite social and cultural competence.

Patients only present themselves to doctors when they feel ill, and have decided that the doctor can do something about it. Having so decided, patients represent their illness in terms of their own concepts. These vary quite strikingly from culture to culture. Those who are ill may thus complain of such things as fevers, chills, nervous upsets, accumulations of gas or festering blood, and account for them using theories about germs, humorous malignant spirits and other alleged causative agents. The details vary enormously and some presentations may seem quite bizarre.

Before they began their training all doctors will have been socialized into particular traditions, whose conventions they will almost certainly continue to utilize to order their own personal and domestic lives. Illness that is expressed in these familiar terms is much more immediately comprehensible than that presented in other ways. Hence English middle-class doctors do not feel that English middle-class representations of illness are at all odd. It is only when they encounter patients who differ from themselves that they may begin to feel that they have a cultural problem on their hands.

If, as is usually the case, doctors are largely unaware that they are actually using a *taken for granted* cultural code to achieve communication with patients who are like themselves, it is easy for them to make fundamental mistakes about the difficulties which they encounter in their dealings with those who differ. Most particularly they can fall into the trap of labelling apparently incomprehensible behaviour as *problem behaviour. Inability to speak English, lack of understanding of modern hygiene, hypochondriasis, superstition, over-protectiveness* may all be brought together under the convenient heading of *social pathology.* Such judgements contain a large measure of ethnocentrism. More often than not they may reflect a lack of cultural competence on the part of practitioners, leading them to regard anything they do not understand as intrinsically problematic.

Culture and communication

Doctors need to develop the capacity to communicate with *all* their patients, not just those who are culturally similar to themselves. Unless doctors have an understanding of their patients' hopes and fears, of their assumptions about health and illness, about diet and hygiene, and above all of the cultural and linguistic codes which they habitually utilize to express themselves, opportunities for meaningful communication will be very limited, and effective treatment may be impaired.

When doctors have equipped themselves to comprehend the range of cultural conventions which their particular patients utilize, much that would otherwise have seemed mysterious, irritating and obstructive in their behaviour should begin to make sense.

Culture, is not an entity but a vehicle for communication. People do what they do, and say what they say, because it makes sense to them. To come to terms with this, doctors must first learn to comprehend their patients' understanding of their own condition. Only this can provide a starting point for effective mutual communication. Discourse ordered in the doctors' jargon is likely to be largely incomprehensible to patients. Similarly, if treatment requires that patients should change their behaviour, *compliance* is much more likely if the instructions given are sensitive to the patients' everyday lifestyles, and presented in such a way that patients readily understand them. Non-compliance is often attributed to the ignorance or stupidity of patients; very frequently it is the result of doctors' inability to get their message across in terms that their patients comprehend.

Successful practice demands that doctors should seek to come to grips with their patients' constructions of reality: that is what cultural competence is all about. Once doctors, and other professionals, begin to inform themselves about the logic of other people's cultural systems, and also learn to incorporate those understandings into the relationships which they establish with their patients, they can begin to work with, rather than across the grain of unfamiliar cultures. This is precisely what doctors expect to do with 'easy' patients who do not differ from themselves.

Cultural diversity in contemporary Britain

Anyone who practices in a society that differs from that in which they were brought up is confronted by these cultural issues. As most British medical students expect to spend their working lives in Britain, it might seem that cultural diversity is an issue of only peripheral relevance.

This view is mistaken. Britain is far from being a culturally homogeneous society. Like most other contemporary societies, it contains numerous dimensions of diversity. One of the most obvious of these arises from the presence of substantial South Asian and West Indian minorities. Members of these groups, who should not be regarded as immigrants since well over half are British born, now make up about 4% of the country's population. They are especially concentrated residentially in the inner areas of the major conurbations, where they form a substantial proportion of the local populace.

Although it was once widely expected that assimilation would rapidly take place, it is now becoming clear that the process of change is far more complicated. Each minority group is tending to retain a considerable degree of cultural distinctiveness for two main reasons:

(1) most people remain committed to the values into which they were socialized as children, and

(2) the best way of establishing networks of mutual aid is by maintaining links with people who share similar values and assumptions.

Hence ethnic colonies are being established in many British cities. This is not to suggest that Asian and West Indian culture in Britain is a static entity, which simply mimics patterns found in the migrants' homelands. A better view is that both migrants and their children are continuously involved in drawing upon their accumulated cultural experience in order to make the best of current circumstances.

Regardless of one's judgements about the rights and wrongs of these social processes, the plain fact is that doctors in many inner city areas find that a substantial proportion of their patients are drawn from one of these minorities. In Bradford, for instance, some 30% of births are now to Asian mothers. Very many of them speak little English, refuse English food, and have their own distinctive ideas about child rearing, personal hygiene, modesty and so forth. In such a context the cultural issues outlined here are very much alive. Perinatal mortality rates amongst such births are three times higher than in the rest of the population, which suggests that current services may not yet be sufficiently attuned to cultural diversity.

Although both differences, and difficulties, tend to be dramatically obvious for South Asian patients, similar issues arise in a large number of other contexts. There are many other smaller groups whose members have recently migrated to Britain, such as Cypriots, Nigerians, Yemenis and Somalis. And other long-settled groups, such as the Irish, the Jews and the Gypsies, have also remained distinct, especially in the way in which they organize their personal family lives.

Perhaps most significantly of all, the truly indigenous population of Britain is not homogeneous either. English, Scots and Welsh lifestyles differ from one another; while midde-class cultural adaptations differ quite sharply from those found in a myriad of distinctive working-class communities. The differences may seem to be less dramatic here than in the case of the ethnic minorities, but the principles are just as important.

Responding to diversity

The conclusion that doctors should respond differently to patients of differing backgrounds stands in sharp contradiction to the widely held view that professionals ought to respond primarily to individual need, irrespective of the race, class, creed or sex of the sufferer. Indeed it is often suggested that for reasons of social justice, doctors ought to approach their patients in as uniform a way as possible, and that any deviation from this idea is necessarily discriminatory.

The flaw in this argument lies in the fact that it ignores the very simple point that no activity can possibly be *a-cultural*. Whether or not practitioners are conscious of it, their practice is necessarily ordered in terms of a particular set of cultural assumptions. Hence all those who organize their lives in culturally distinctive ways, whether they be members of an ethnic minority or of a working-class community, may be placed at a disadvantage. Rigid uniformity in practice does not necessarily promote equality, it often institutionalizes inequality.

All this raises important questions about the proper basis for good professional practice in a culturally diverse society. In dealing with their patients medical staff find it easiest to apply the cultural framework with which they themselves are most familiar. Yet such a strategy inevitably hampers communication with those who differ. Doctors who adopt the alternative solution, learning to understand and work with their patients on their patients' own terms, can expect greater achievement in treatment. In so far as cultural diversity is intrinsic to our humanity, cultural competence is quite as vital a medical skill as is sheer technical excellence.

Further reading:

Henley A. (1979) *Asian Patients at Hospital and at Home*. London, The King's Fund.
Lewis I.M. (1971) *Social Anthropology in Perspective*. Harmondsworth, Penguin.
Watson J.L. (Ed.) (1977) *Between Two Cultures: Migrants and Minorities in Britain*. Oxford, Basil Blackwell.
Rack P. (1982) *Race, Culture and Mental Disorder*. London, Tavistock.

CHAPTER 4

Human Learning

Human learning

The study of learning is central to any attempt at achieving a comprehensive understanding of human behaviour, simply because most human behaviour is learned. The term *learning* refers to the process underlying any relatively permanent change in behaviour, or the probability of occurrence of a particular behaviour resulting from experience; this excludes behaviour change resulting from damage to the central nervous system. The experience may be secondhand; hence the importance of language in the communication of information and experience, and the vastly superior capacity for change and adaptation shown by humans compared with other species.

Learning is a hypothetical process or set of processes, whose activity has to be inferred from changes in behaviour. There is, at present, no consensus about the physiological or biochemical substrates of learning.

It is important to distinguish learning from *maturation*, which refers to a biologically determined change in behaviour that follows a defined time course. Maturation of a function has to occur before learned control of that function can take place. Thus toilet training or speech cannot be learned until the relevant physiological and neural components have matured. On the other hand, control of bowel movements and speech mechanisms does not develop unless the opportunity to learn them is present. A child brought up in a silent world does not learn to speak.

Most human behaviour is learned; the contribution of unlearned behaviour patterns to the total behaviour repertoire decreases as we go up in the phylogenetic scale. This means that flexibility in response to environmental demands increases, so that in humans it is likely that any unlearned aspect of behaviour is overridden. The term *instinct* is often used to refer to relatively complex unlearned behaviour patterns, such as some aspects of social and reproductive behaviour. The study of these behaviours in non-human species in the natural setting is known as *ethology*.

Classical conditioning

Conventionally two schemes are identified for the organisation of the conditions under which learning is likely to occur. The first is concerned with physiological responses that are normally elicited by a single, definable stimulus, for example pupil constriction to a light stimulus, or salivation to food in the mouth. These are un-learned, *pre-programmed*, associations. If a neutral stimulus is now presented together with the *natural* stimulus a sufficient number of times, it develops the property of eliciting the response on its own. This is *classical, Pavlovian or respondent learning (or conditioning)*. The original pairing is between the *unconditional stimulus* (UCS), for example a light shone in the eye, and the *unconditional response* (UCR), the constriction of the pupil. The learned association is between the *conditional stimulus* (CS), for example the ringing of a bell, and the *conditional response* (CR), which is, to all intents and purposes identical with the UCR. In this example, ringing a bell that has no prior links with pupil constriction, comes to elicit this response from its association with the light. The central concept here is that of *association*, or contiguity. Because of the ease with which physiological responses may be associated with a wide variety of previously neutral stimuli, classical conditioning is of the utmost importance in the learning of emotional responses and the possible genesis of some psychosomatic or psychophysiological conditions. This is considered more fully in Chapter 10.

Operant conditioning

The second set of conditions is more obviously to do with human behaviour; the likelihood of a particular behaviour taking place depends upon its predicted consequences. An act is said to be re-warded or reinforced, and is likely to be learned, if it is followed by desired consequences or is subjectively satisfying. In contrast to the passive nature of classical conditioning, the subject here has to do something actively, to operate on the environment, in order to achieve a reward. Hence the use of the term *operant conditioning* to refer to this set of conditions. The name of Skinner is most often associated with operant methodology. We can identify a number of important variations on this theme. *Escape learning* is where a response is reinforced because it terminates a noxious stimulus (this is negative reinforcement). *Avoidance learning* on the other hand involves the learning of a response which prevents the occurrence of a predicted or signalled noxious stimulus. Where the noxious stimulus is contingent upon, and follows a particular response, then that response is said to be punished.

The time relations between a response and its consequences are crucial in determining the strength of any resultant learning. Generally speaking, the immediate consequences of a behaviour are more likely to determine the future display of that behaviour than any consequences more distant in time. Thus, the satisfying feelings following the smoking of a cigarette now, are more important for the continuation of the smoking habit, than the (presumed) punishment of severe chronic illness some time in the future.

Stimulus control

Behaviour does not occur in a vacuum, or at random. It is elicited by, or is contingent upon, aspects of the current environment. In this sense behaviour can be said to be under the control of certain environmental stimuli. These are called *discriminative stimuli*. They can be positive or negative, having either an excitatory or inhibitory effect upon behaviour. For example, being with other students drinking beer in a pub could provide a set of discriminative stimuli for getting drunk, whereas being with the same students, drinking sherry in the house of a consultant physician would probably constitute a set of negative discriminatory stimuli for such behaviour and inhibit it. It is a commonplace enough observation that the same person behaves differently in different situations: studiously in the library; attentively in lectures; reverently on the ward round; boisterously at a party. Part of the explanation for this variety of behaviour lies in the properties of the different situations, that is, the various discriminative stimuli as perceived by the person concerned.

There are two further points of importance to note. First, the same stimulus can have different consequences, and therefore different implications for behaviour for different people, depending on their individual learning histories. Observations of cultural variation in response to identical situations, for instance illness and death, demonstrate the validity of this point. Secondly, the stimulus is that which is perceived by the subject, and not necessarily what is 'really' there. Related to this is the fact that perception is not always at a conscious level. Our behaviour is known to be affected by stimuli which are outside the range of our awareness. Any situation is made up of a large number of discrete stimuli, any one of which could serve as a discriminative stimulus for a particular behaviour. The possibility then arises that a situation could contain both positive and negative stimuli for the same behaviour. Under these conditions conflict is likely to ensue, a topic which is covered in more detail in Chapter 17.

Although initially a particular stimulus tends to be associated with a particular response, this association becomes more flexible. We then find that a behaviour can be elicited by a stimulus which was like, but not identical to, the original conditional stimulus. This phenomenon is called *stimulus generalisation* and is of vital importance to human behaviour. Because no two situations are ever precisely the same, stimulus generalisation allows us to see similarities between situations, and to behave as though they were the same. As a consequence we do not have to learn about each new environment from scratch, we can utilise our memories of similar environments. This is a property which clearly has survival value. Taken together, generalisation and discrimination provide the organism with the potential to respond adaptively to a wide range of stimuli. Generalisation allows us to perceive the similiarities between environments, while discrimination is concerned with the differences, thus allowing the development of an adaptive control over behaviour.

Drives and learning

While discriminative stimuli may be considered to direct behaviour from outside the person, it is necessary to explain why behaviour occurs at all. Most theories postulate the action of energising forces which have their origins within the person. They are usually referred to as *drives* or needs. The relevance of drives to learning is that the drive state of a person determines which set of stimuli, out of the large number available at any one time, will be perceived as rewarding. For example, if I am not hungry, I am unlikely to perceive food as a reward; whereas if I have been deprived of food, it then becomes more meaningful to me. If I am unsure of myself doing a particular job, the praise of colleagues or patients is more rewarding than a salary increase, and makes it more likely that I will continue. Drives are usually classified into two groups:

(1) primary drives relating to the maintenance of the physical well-being of the individual, such as those to do with food and comfort; and

(2) secondary drives, relating to a person's psychological well-being.

This latter includes drives to do with self-esteem, achievement, friendship, and so on.

Clearly for most people in Western culture, the satisfaction of primary drives is taken for granted, and most of our behaviour is related to the satisfaction of secondary drives, which are probably learned. For example, in babies, feeding is a social situation, associated with the presence of another person. It is also associated with the reduction of a primary hunger drive and the consequent satisfying feelings become associated with the stimulus 'being with another person'. Because of this association, this stimulus takes on drive properties, the presence of another person being rewarding, and we have the origins of a *friendship* drive, or perhaps a *dependency* drive. The resultant drive, of course, depends upon the nature of the interaction. This analysis is not to suggest that friendship or dependency always originate in this way, or that early experiences always have a profound effect on later behaviour, but it does suggest a model for the development of secondary drives and an explanation of the wide range of individual differences observed in this context.

Behaviour that is not reinforced decreases in frequency until it disappears, provided the reinforcement is not forthcoming. This is a process known as *extinction*. Mothers of attention-seeking children have known about it for years. The rate of extinction varies depending on the way in which the behaviour had previously been reinforced. Once a behaviour has been established, that is, there is a high probability of its occurrence given the appropriate stimulus, it can be maintained by intermittent reinforcement. Here, not every response but only a small percentage is reinforced. Under these conditions, it becomes quite difficult for the response to be extinguished when the reinforcement is permanently removed. This is clearly a state of affairs which applies to much of human behaviour in real life: reinforcement is not always forthcoming after every response, and most behaviours once established are quite difficult to change. The implications for health-related behaviours is examined more fully in Chapter 29.

This chapter has considered some of the more important concepts of learning, and introduced the most frequently encountered technical terms. Many of these concepts will be met again in succeeding chapters, as learning is seen to play a central role in the determination of behaviour in both health and ill-health.

Further reading:

Hilgard E.R., Atkinson R.C. & Atkinson R.L. (1979) *Introduction to Psychology*, 7th Edition. New York, Harcourt Brace Jovanovich.

CHAPTER 5

Perception and Attention

Perception and attention

Perception may be defined as the organisation of *sensory experiences* into a meaningful, orderly arrangement of objects and events in time and space; or, more concisely, perception is a *cognitive response* to *sensory input*. It is not simply the sum of integrated sensory experiences. Certain characteristics of the perceptual process, of subjective experiences, are based on minimal sensory cues. For example, a two-dimensional sketch or photograph may be perceived as having perspective and depth. It is also possible for identical patterns of sensation to give rise to very different perceptions from one individual or another or from occasion to occasion for the same individual (Fig. 5.1). Perception may also involve more or less than the available sensory information. The organisation of sensory experiences into a cognition is referred to as a *percept* and is the outcome of an active process.

Value of perception

Perception has survival value. The ability to organise sensations into a meaningful percept influenced by past experience can enable adaptive action to occur. For example, seeing a moving object flying rapidly through the air towards you and recognising it as dangerous can enable you to duck in time. Sherrington pointed out that all the *distance receptors* were in the head and hence had the shortest nerve pathway to the brain thus permitting a longer time to be available to make sense of experience.

As well as having survival value, perceptual processes facilitate the *orientation* of the individual in space. It is possible to combine

26

various sensory cues, of visible objects and their relationship to each other with other types of sensory experiences, for example with position sense to form a percept that maintains personal orientation in space. Through such means the individual protects himself and takes advantage of his external environment.

FIG. 5.1.   Reversible image (after Escher).

Perception is also valuable when combined with memory processes to enable the individual to sustain himself. Since identical sensory inputs are very unlikely to occur on subsequent occasions, we never see things exactly the same way twice, and it is necessary therefore that images or *concepts* evolve which express the essential qualities of what is sensed. Thus a primitive hunter might leave his shelter in search of food and what is more, recognise his quarry as such when he finds it despite never having seen this particular animal before.

Acquisition of percepts

There are three major factors which can influence the acquisition of a percept.

(1) *Qualities* of the *external world*; for example we might see certain colours in full daylight which appear simply as grey at dusk.

(2) The *efficiency* of our *sense receptors*. It is well recognised that individuals who are hard of hearing misperceive what may be said in conversation.

(3) The nature of the *person* who is doing the *perceiving*. Clinical research reveals that certain noxious stimuli are perceived as painful by the majority of people, and yet can be erotic or exciting for others.

It is apparent that we organise and make sense of our world in highly idiosyncratic ways. We add bits, ignore bits, and fit bits together in an individual manner to produce personal meaning. Maturational and developmental processes play a significant part since experiences are interpreted differently as we become older.

It is possible to exercise a certain amount of deliberate control over what is sensed. The eyes may be closed, fingers put in the ears, hands withdrawn from touching objects. More interestingly it is possible to direct attention selectively. The viewer at an art gallery does not look at a painting in its entirety, but pays attention to parts that catch the eye, thus building up an image that has both visual and emotive meaning. Conversations take place on noisy tube trains or buses because the participants are able to attend selectively to part of the total sensory information. Surgeons can project their sense of touch to the end of a scalpel or probe so that, although they may only feel a metal implement through a rubber glove, they can perceive consistency and structure in the tissues of the patient.

Many percepts carry with them emotional qualities. Generally speaking sensations experienced as smooth, warm and soft are perceived as good while rough, cold, hard sensations are negatively appraised. Sensory inputs are always mixed involving experiences from different sense organs. Combinations of sensory input from different sense organs are more open to the acquisition of emotional associations, while at the same time are more likely to be retained or learned. This is most obvious in the perception of possible danger or threat. The recognition that fire is dangerous is very soon learned, not necessarily as the result of directly painful experience. Perceptual processes may thus facilitate adaptation to the environment.

Dimensions of perception

It is necessary to refer to texts on physiology to understand better the function of the sense organs, but certain dimensions of sensory experience are important in relation to perception:

(1) intensity,
(2) duration, (both 1 and 2 are common to all sense modalities),
(3) qualitative differences across modalities, and
(4) adaptation.

The human sensory apparatus has boundaries above or below which sensory input may not be consciously experienced. Within these limits of awareness it is important to know the extent to which subjective experience coincides with the physical qualities of the stimulus: its intensity and duration. For example, low frequency sounds are commonly perceived as being much louder than high frequency sounds of the same amplitude. Sometimes signals in one sensory modality are experienced in another, for instance, loud noises are experienced as pain; certain people perceive musical sounds as colours. There is also the consideration of how much a stimulus needs to be increased or decreased in order for it to be perceived as having altered.

Weber's Law stated that the size of increment (or decrement) of a stimulus necessary for it to be subjectively experienced as having changed, bore a constant relationship to the intensity of the initial stimulus. This rule or law was later modified by Fechner to allow for the findings that occurred at the extremes of the range of sensation, and has been stated as $S = K \log R$, that is the changes necessary to experience a difference in the stimulus (S) bears a constant relationship to the logarithm of the original stimulus value (R). Broadly speaking this generalisation appears to hold true for different sense modalities. For instance, a patient suffering from an extremely painful broken leg may not perceive any additional pain caused by efforts to reduce the fracture; in contrast a very sensitive individual complaining loudly about an insect sting may react dramatically to the prick of a hypodermic needle. In a noisy discotheque the music would have to be increased considerably to be noticed as having become louder, while even a creaking board at night time may be sufficient to waken a light sleeper.

Only part of the available sensory input is perceived, and even this is interpreted in a highly subjective manner. This can be clearly demonstrated observing a radiologist inspecting X-ray pictures or a pathologist looking down his microscope. When medical students inspect histological sections under a microscope, they may be told what might be seen, and stains are used to facilitate this perception. Without being told what to perceive, many would fail to identify anything meaningful. What happens is that active encouragement is given to the formation of a *set* so that attention is selectively directed to identify particular aspects of the stimulus. Of course it is possible to acquire an unwanted set so that sensory inputs are wrongly perceived. The avid bird watcher may report hearing the first cuckoo of spring when in fact he may only have heard a turtle dove.

Constancy of percepts

On the grounds of survival value alone, it is obviously important to have an awareness of the environment and to note any changes in it. Yet percepts do have certain characteristics which would suggest that direct experience of the external world is a rarity and changes have to be quite marked before they are noticed. Percepts demonstrate *constancy*. That is, they continue to be perceived in the same manner although the sensory experience may never be the same on two occasions. For example, it is easy to recognise a bus in the street despite the fact that it is most unlikely to have been sensed in an identical setting in the past. Lighting conditions change all the time, the orientation of the bus towards the perceiver alters; the colour, shape and sounds emitted by the bus vary and yet we are able to recognise the object to be a bus. The learning process by which certain sensory signals consistently elicit the percept of a bus are very complex. Even a fairly young child refrains from trying to stop motor cars or lorries in the street with the intention of boarding them, though in certain circumstances the child may be uncertain about particular vehicles, for example an ambulance. It is the constancy phenomenon which can sometimes lead to surprise when things prove not to be as they are expected to be. Many illusions can be explained in terms of perceptual constancy.

An illusion can be defined as the misperception of sensory cues. The seemingly moving pictures seen at the cinema are in fact a series of still pictures projected at around twenty-four exposures per second. Many illusions are created out of the expectancies of the perceiver, perhaps enhanced by sensory cues provided by the background. An interesting illusion is déjà vu, or false memory of having been somewhere before; sufficient stimuli are present to elicit recollections from many previous experiences resulting in an overall composite false impression of memory for a new situation.

Meaning of percepts

Stimuli are usually perceived in groups or as being related to one another. A splendid example of this is the astrological map of the heavens where quite unrelated stars are grouped together simply because they appear to make a meaningful shape in the sky. The tendency to organise sensations into a meaningful whole or pattern is referred to as forming a *Gestalt*. Many parts of the sensorium may be added, altered or omitted in this process of forming a Gestalt.

A particularly interesting phenomenon is referred to as figure-ground discrimination. We are readily able to discriminate an object from its background; indeed this may be so exaggerated in some people, for example a spider phobic, that they only identify the figure/object and hardly recognise anything about the background against which it is perceived. In other circumstances it sometimes happens that a figure is generally perceived against a particular background, and then suddenly the perception shifts so that the background becomes the figure and the figure becomes the background. Some ancients spoke of the stars being distant lamps hung before the backcloth of night, while others spoke of the stars as providing a glimpse of paradise seen through tiny holes in the heavens.

Differences across sensory modalities

There is good evidence to suggest that visual information is of primary importance to humans. On occasions visual sensations can override other sensory input in the production of a percept. For example, a normal 50 pence piece seen through reducing lenses may be handled, weighed and thoroughly examined by touch, but the verbal report of what has been perceived may be: 'a small copy of a 50 pence coin.' Oddly enough when we wish to manipulate concepts in consciousness, even those percepts derived entirely from visual experiences, we tend to do so verbally. At the same time it is well recognised that we see what we expect to see. In other words, previous learning plays a great part in perception. An architect examining house plans perceives more than the average person. Information is added and even lines seen which are not there in fact. We are used to seeing objects illuminated from above, and when faced with interpreting a picture of an irregular object lit from below, for instance a telescopic photograph of the moon, then craters are perceived as mountains and hills as indentations. By turning such a picture upside down so that the light source appears to come as expected from the top the real state of affairs may be perceived.

Disorders of perception

The process of perception is a very sophisticated activity and is subject to disturbance resulting from many kinds of illness. Transient confusion of sensory organisation is commonly observed following loss of consciousness whether as a result of a blow to the head or of anaesthesia during operation. Altered consciousness may produce many kinds of misperceptions including misidentification of other persons and very peculiar experiences of believing oneself to be in some different environment. Some individuals take deliberate steps to alter their own levels of consciousness by using toxic substances which produce distortions of perception. Brain damage may produce long lasting or permanent disorder of perceptual processes. Here, the location of the damage is more important than the extent in determining disturbance of perception. *Dyspraxia*, which is difficulty in carrying out coordinated voluntary movements, often occurs with *agnosia*, a perceptual disturbance in which objects cannot be recognised adequately although there is no peripheral sensory deficit. *Constructional dyspraxia* can be most readily demonstrated by inviting the sufferer to reproduce visual patterns by copying, or to complete a simple jig-saw.

Perceptual disturbances are often observed in patients suffering from certain psychiatric illnesses when there is no impairment of sensory apparatus. Auditory hallucinations occur in schizophrenia, especially the hearing of voices or meaningful sounds experienced as coming from outside the person as if from an external source. An *hallucination* may be defined as a perceptual experience without the presence of appropriate sensory stimulation.

Disturbances of perception are also reported to occur in far less serious psychological disorders. Depressed people complain that they find it hard to concentrate and pay attention to matters in hand, and they also may complain that colours look drab, and that food has no taste. Obsessional people say they cannot get their mind off their ruminations which occupy more and more of their time. Phobic patients regularly have illusory experiences that serve to trigger their fears, a housewife who dreads mice may well misperceive any small object on the floor as being a mouse.

In conclusion, it must be stressed that perceptual processes are central to our personal understanding of, and relationship with, other people. The evidence suggests that initial visual impressions are of primary importance in our perception of others. These visual experiences are influenced by learning and expectancies so that affect becomes attached to the neutral source of sensory signals. To put it simply, when we meet someone in hospital labelled as a doctor, we compare the direct visual experience with what we expect a doctor to look like, and to be. It is well recognised that patients perceive qualities in doctors that may not be there and that these illusions may be used by healers for the good. In contrast, if there should be too great a clash between expectation and experience, for example the young doctor happens to have a Mohican haircut and wear ear-rings, then it is likely that the patients will not respond in a favourable manner no matter how clever, skilled, personable or enthusiastic that doctor might be. Although lip-service is paid to the importance of qualities of personality or sense of humour and the like, in our evaluations of others it is the first visual impressions that seem to dominate. Experimental evidence derived from comparing the effectiveness of auditory with visual information in communication favours the latter.

CHAPTER 6

Intelligence

Intelligence

Intelligence or intellectual capacity is of immense importance to human beings. The English language abounds with descriptions and synonyms for the possession, or lack, of intelligence, such as bright, clever, quick-witted, sharp, smart. It is a highly desirable attribute, since clearly the adjectives which describe its absence, such as dull, stupid, or slow, carry pejorative implications.

The development of a concept of intelligence

Galton, one of the first to investigate intelligence in a laboratory setting believed that problem-solving behaviour demonstrated two distinct human characteristics. The first he called 'ability' and the second 'zeal'. He believed each individual possessed a certain inherited level of 'ability' as well as a range of potential aptitudes which could be modified by environmental factors. He suggested that education was concerned with modifying 'zeal' or motivation and interest which in turn influenced the extent to which an individual could bring his 'ability' to bear upon a problem.

This view of intelligence has affected psychology in Britain more permanently than in the rest of the world. Binet in Paris, 1905, was set a definite practical problem. He was asked to estimate how many children might be too dull to benefit from compulsory primary education which had recently been introduced by the French government. He argued that it was justifiable to ignore motivational factors in his examination of problem-solving behaviour by school children because all of them should be maximally motivated by the examiners at the time of testing. The problems themselves

34

were believed to assess basic abilities as opposed to particular aptitudes or special skills. In fact the tasks revealed a high incidence of educational items, though they also seemed to tap more fundamental reasoning abilities. The important contribution that Binet brought to the attempt to assess intelligence was the concept of *mental age*. Together with his co-workers he established the average scores produced by children of different ages. Later the simple formula $\frac{MA}{CA} \times 100$ = Intelligence Quotient (IQ) was introduced, where MA = mental age, and CA = chronological age. Obviously if a child performed at a rather better level than might have been expected from his chronological age then the IQ would be greater than 100, and vice versa. An IQ of 100 would indicate an average level of performance, for that age group.

The Binet scales met a need in the world of education and were exported and modified for use in many countries. Updated versions of these scales are still in use today. In the United Kingdom, however the tradition set by Galton continued to pervade psychological circles and attempts to define and measure intelligence persisted.

Spearman, for example, used reasoning tasks, practical problems, and also measures of psychomotor performance, reaction times, coordination tests and the like. He sought to demonstrate that there was a general factor of intelligence or *g* present in the solution of all problems to a greater or lesser extent. Some tasks required a lot of *g* in their resolution, while others seemed to require little *g* but were very dependent upon acquired aptitudes or special skills. One of the outcomes of this work was a somewhat modified definition of what was meant by intelligence. Spearman perceived it as a type of reasoning ability and spoke of it as the ability to perceive correlates, to induce principles and to make correct predictions based upon them. His definition seems very like the description of scientific method. Another very important product of Spearman's work was the gradual evolution of statistical method, in particular the concept of correlation and the factor analytic method.

The mental tests employed by Spearman and others were believed to sample aspects of problem-solving behaviour. Questions inevitably arose as to whether these mental tests were measuring what they claimed to measure (validity), and secondly, were measurements of any enduring characteristic or liable to alter on the next occasion of testing (reliability). The issue of *validity* is most important in the application of any measuring device, especially when the measurement can not be made directly, unlike many physical sciences. Measurement in psychology or the social sciences can only be correlational as the quality being assessed is usually not amenable to the direct application of a measuring implement. In much of psychological measurement what is sought is predictive validity. In other words, did Binet's tests, for example, in fact succeed in discriminating the educable child from the ineducable? A follow-up experiment would have been required to test this out, though it can be seen that *contamination* would have been an issue since the results of the original measures would have brought about differential educational opportunities for the children, and this would in turn affect the follow-up findings.

The second issue of *reliability* is more open to examination. By reliability is meant the extent to which a measurement is consistent both from occasion to occasion and from one assessor to another. It is pointless to evolve an intelligence test that is subject to the transient moods or whims of the person being assessed, so that a score obtained one day is quite independent of a score obtained on another occasion. Intelligence is presumed to be a stable individual characteristic. In such circumstances it can be appreciated that the validity of such a test must be very low indeed. It would also seem important that a measure should not vary according to who happened to be using it at a particular time. This aspect of reliability is sometimes forgotten in medicine so that it is possible for a wide range of blood pressures to be derived from the same patient over a short space of time according to who happens to be using the sphygmomanometer.

The sophistication of the measurement of intelligence

Efforts to define better what was meant by intelligence continued unabated over the 60 years after Spearman's innovations in the realm of measurement. Certain broad trends have emerged, notably the difference between the search for pure *g* in the U.K. and the attention given to special aptitudes in the U.S.A.. In Britain there have been great efforts to develop *culture fair* tests and techniques for the *partialling-out* of the effects of special factors like education or social class. One product of this research has been group tests like the *Progressive Matrices* which proved to be very useful in the selection and allocation of recruits to the armed forces in World War II. In contrast American work has aimed at the identification of the many aspects of intelligent behaviour that go towards successful adjustment in that society. In the 1930s Thurstone developed tests of five primary mental abilities that he believed to have good predictive qualities in terms of adjustment to the environment. In 1946 Wechsler in New York produced a relatively large test battery for the assessment of individual subjects and defined intelligence as 'the global capacity of the individual to act purposefully, to think rationally and to deal effectively with his environment'. These tests, the Wechsler Adult Intelligence Scale (WAIS) and the Wechsler Intelligence Scale for Children (WISC) cover a wide range of abilities or aptitudes and produce three main scores: a measure of verbal reasoning that is heavily weighted with educational and social factors; a measure of practical problem-solving that involves speed as well as visual perceptual abilities; and, an overall score that purports to reflect Wechsler's definition of intelligence.

More importantly Wechsler produced a somewhat improved method of deriving an IQ score. Binet's concept of mental age ran into difficulties at the top of the children's age range. The average test score reached a maximum in the early twenties of the adult range and the mental age: chronological age ratio became meaningless. Wechsler's innovation amounted to defining the average score for any particular group as being equivalent to IQ 100 and then attributing IQ scores above and below average according to the statistical distribution giving one standard deviation the equivalent of fifteen points of IQ. It was an obvious improvement as it now became possible to assess any individual against the distribution of his particular age group and as a consequence note any changes that might occur from testing to testing.

In general terms there are three broad types of definition of intelligence in the contemporary literature:

(1) definitions that emphasise adaptation or adjustment to an individual's environment,

(2) definitions associated with an individual's ability to learn from experience and to bring this learning to bear upon immediate problem-solving, and

(3) definitions which focus upon the ability to carry out abstract reasoning involving the use of symbolic thinking and the manipulation of concepts.

Detailed research into the content of intelligence test responses has been carried out by Guilford. He came to the conclusion that many factors contribute to the production of a test score, and proposed a morphological model of intelligence at the pinnacle of which is g or pure intelligence. Guilford stressed that intelligence is a quality of man as defined by psychologists and is very largely a theoretical construct which adds some meaning to everyday language used by non-psychologists but is hardly an entity in itself. On the other hand he did imply that at the pure g end of the continuum there should be some correlation with cortical development and sophistication of the brain. It is noticeable that when intelligence is measured by any of the reliable techniques a bell-shaped, normal distribution of scores is produced, as it is with measures of any other biological variable. However, closer inspection of the distribution reveals that there are too many individuals in the lower half of the curve. Brain damage moves scores on an intelligence test in a downward direction; at the lower end of the distribution curve there is a higher incidence of individuals with brain disease, and it seems probable that intelligence has a physical basis in the brain.

Uses of intelligence tests

Intelligence testing has had many practical uses, not all of them desirable. Until fairly recent times it was argued that 'bright' children merited special educational provisions and were selected to attend certain types of school. Many now believe this to have been politically and socially a mistake. Other children were deemed ineducable on the basis of intelligence tests and presented as a problem for the health services outside educational provision. Organisations concerned with the mentally handicapped have successfully argued that what is required is special education and not hospital care, except in circumstances of multiple physical and mental handicap. There is some evidence to suggest that the so-called problems of lack of intelligence are really difficulties in communication. Certain mentally handicapped persons have great problems in learning because they can only retain information for very brief moments of time and hence cannot transfer it to long-term store where it might be available to be called upon for use in other situations to cope with problem solving. Other people, those with spastic dysarthria, may appear mentally subnormal simply because they cannot communicate or carry out simple tasks. Nonetheless, detailed examination of cognitive functioning still has its place in the assessment of individuals who appear to lack intelligence.

An interesting application of testing has been in the assessment of the ageing process. It was noted in the early years of intelligence test development that maximum scores appeared to be reached in the 20-year-old age groups after which scores remained fairly constant until the last decades of life when the average scores apparently fell steadily. It was suggested that the test scores reflected a gradual deterioration of mental functioning in later life. More recent longitudinal studies have suggested that this may well not be the case and could be the result of *cross-sectional sampling*. That is, in any group of 60 + years some individuals will be suffering from cortical degeneration due to a range of possible causes and the average scores obtained from such a group reveal an apparent decline as compared with a cross section of 50 year olds. As age progresses so the incidence of cortical diseases increases and the average scores fall. The longitudinal studies imply that for individuals who remain relatively healthy there is apparently no obvious decline in intellectual abilities. Further than this, the research suggests that it may be possible to arrest or slow down the rate of decline by remaining mentally active and engaging in intellectually stimulating pursuits. At the same time it has generally been observed in all the studies that the peak of intellectual achievement in the sense of pure g seems to be reached in the age range 18–25 years after which continued improvement seems to lie in the acquisition of special aptitudes notably verbal concepts and reasoning skills.

CHAPTER 7

Localization of Function in the Brain

There are two major and, at times, conflicting, current views of brain function. On the one hand there is the view that the brain acts as a whole so that injury to a particular part is overcome by those parts which remain intact: this has come to be known as the *aggregate field* view of cerebral functioning. This view stems from the work of Flourens, and has been associated with the names of Head, Goldstein and, in recent times, that of Lashley. The alternative view is that particular activities are localized in the brain with certain areas having discrete functions mediated by specific neural pathways. This view of brain function has been called *cellular connectionism*, and is associated with the names of Hughlings-Jackson, Wernicke, Cajal, Jacobsen and Penfield. Neither view has proved entirely satisfactory. The nervous system clearly has the capacity to function after sustaining severe damage, and for certain complex functions to be taken over by other areas. Furthermore, it is apparent that no part of the brain functions in isolation from its other parts, and that removal of a part of the brain does not lead to consistent deficiencies which clearly reflect its normal functions.

Localization of motor and sensory functions (Fig. 7.1)

In 1861 Broca reported the case of a patient who could not speak himself but was able to understand the speech of others. At postmortem examination the brain showed a lesion in the posterior portion of the frontal lobe; a region which has come to be known as *Broca's area*. In eight further cases a similar syndrome was seen with the lesion on the left in seven of the eight subjects. Broca noted that the eighth patient was left handed, and this observation

led to the notion of a crossed relationship between cerebral dominance and hand preference.

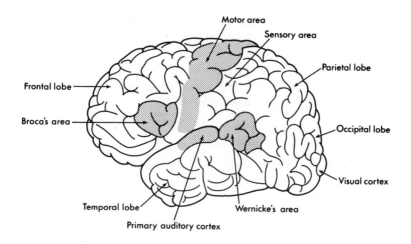

FIG. 7.1.   Location of sensory and motor areas.

Subsequently Fritsch and Hitzig reported that stimulation of the
precentral gyrus in dogs gave rise to movements of the limbs. This
finding led to the mapping of the motor cortex, extending knowledge of localization of function in the cortex of most motor
activities. Soon afterwards, in 1876, Wernicke described a patient
who could speak but not understand speech, and the lesion associated with this syndrome was situated in the posterior part of the
temporal lobe, or *Wernicke's area*. He suggested that the functions
of speaking and understanding speech are located in two specific
areas in the dominant hemisphere which work in parallel; possibly
in association with other areas of the brain. He postulated the
existence of a syndrome of *conduction aphasia* caused by lesions of
structures connecting the two more specific areas, and lying in the
parietal area. This syndrome was subsequently recognized clinically.

In spite of the evidence suggesting localization of certain brain functions there was little to suggest localization of higher functions such as learning, emotional expression, intellectual tasks and aspects of behaviour. Lashley's experiments, in which he examined learning in rats, failed to demonstrate areas of the brain which were specifically concerned with learning; there appeared to be an impairment of learning which was related to the amount of tissue removed rather than to the site from which it was taken. However, in the 1950s the weight of evidence swung back in favour of localization of function following Penfield's findings on the effects of electrical stimulation of the brain in conscious human subjects. He confirmed the findings of Broca and Wernicke and elaborated the findings in animals of Fritsch and Hitzig.

Localization of higher functions

Recent views of higher functions have stressed the importance of the integration of the activities of the various structural and functional regions of the brain. Nevertheless, certain parts of the brain appear to be especially concerned in certain higher cerebral activities. The frontal, temporal and parietal lobes particularly are thought to be concerned in higher functions and are known as the association areas of the cortex.

Lesions in the *frontal lobes* of monkeys may lead to difficulties in performing complex delayed spatial tasks. Of greater clinical significance is the observation by Jacobsen that prefrontal lesions altered the emotional responsiveness of monkeys, making them calm and unable to show rage and anger. Lesions in the *medial orbital cortex* showed this effect most markedly. These findings eventually led to operations in which the same fibre tracts were interrupted surgically in man to reduce or control violent or disturbed behaviour in patients suffering from severe psychiatric disorders. Unfortunately there were some unwanted effects of these operations, including postoperative epilepsy, changes in personality and a lack of initiative and drive. The clinical value of these procedures is now disputed and their use is restricted to a very small number of subjects.

As has been already outlined, the *temporal lobes* are associated with sensory functions. The primary auditory projection area is in the superior part of the temporal lobe (*Brodman's area 41*) and the posterior part of the lobe is associated with language (Wernicke's area). Much of the lobe consists of association areas: the superior part related to the auditory system, and the middle and inferior portions to visual functions. Lesions in the inferior part of the lobes impair learning of visual material especially where this is complex. Inferior temporal lesions appear to impair the retention of information particularly severely. Similarly lesions in the superior temporal region produce difficulty in auditory learning without deafness.

Neurosurgical investigations and operations have provided information on the functioning of the temporal lobes of patients suffering from temporal lobe epilepsy. Penfield confirmed that stimulation of the superior temporal area produced auditory sensations; some of these experiences were complex in form. In patients where the temporal lobes were removed there was impairment of the capacity to form long-term memories, and where the operation was bilateral the degree of impairment was severe. The effect was not the same on the two sides: where the dominant temporal lobe was removed the deficit was most severe in the retention of verbal material but in the case of the non-dominant lobe there were difficulties in retaining patterns of information. These findings have been paralleled in the study of brain-damaged subjects.

The *parietal lobes* consist of the somatic sensory areas of the postcentral gyrus anteriorly and the much more extensive association areas posteriorly. The association area shows activity during sensory stimulation of an animal, but this is variable and not closely related to the nature of the stimulus. The parietal lobes appear to be concerned with the spatial relationships in sensory input. This idea is supported by clinical observation: patients with parietal lobe lesions show striking disturbances of *body image* and in appreciation of *spatial relationships*. Where the dominant parietal lobe is affected there may be *aphasia* (disorder of language), *agnosia* (inability to comprehend or recognize sensory impressions) and *astereognosis* (loss of the ability to recognize the shape and consistency of objects). Lesions in the non-dominant lobe leave language unaffected but there may be impairment of the spatial relationships of sensations, a lack of appreciation of space to the opposite side of the body, and denial of the existence of the opposite side of the body with its subsequent neglect.

From Broca's time, at least, it has been recognized that all brain functions are not bilaterally represented and that in certain respects each hemisphere may have a specialized function. Certain of these functions are associated with *handedness*. This field has been advanced by the study of human subjects and animals where the hemispheres have become separated by the section of the *corpus callosum*. This is known as the split brain, and may be produced experimentally in animals or in man in the treatment of intractable epilepsy. Myers and Sperry were able to show that the hemispheres function independently, and that the effects of training in one hemisphere are not shared by the other. The preservation of the optic chiasma in human subjects meant that visual learning occurred in both hemispheres simultaneously and deficiencies were only revealed by highly specialized tests. When visual stimuli were limited to the non-dominant hemisphere learning could occur only in non-verbal terms. The right hemisphere can recognize simple verbal messages but not respond verbally. The non-dominant hemisphere, however, is more skilful in the performance of some non-verbal spatial tasks. The hemispheres may interfere with the performance of tasks presented to both; it seems likely that in normal circumstances the hemisphere most fitted to a certain task becomes dominant in its performance. In general terms verbal and intellectual tasks are better performed by the dominant hemisphere; and the non-dominant hemisphere is better in non-verbal, spatial, emotional, and intuitive tasks.

Hemisphere dominance is not developed at birth, and in the young there is potential for either hemisphere to become dominant. Children who suffer brain damage to one hemisphere at birth can develop normal speech and other functions. This capacity is most strikingly seen where young children have a hemisphere removed because of uncontrollable epilepsy: initial deficiencies in speech and other lateralized functions often show remarkable recovery. On the other hand, hemispherectomy in adults is followed by very limited recovery of function suggesting a loss of adaptability of neural function with maturation.

The development of dominance in the hemispheres normally leads to the left hemisphere becoming dominant in man, dominance in the right hemisphere occurs in a small proportion, and incomplete dominance in others. Handedness is not always linked with more general dominance. The development of dominance is thought to be slower in females than in males and may be linked with the frequently described finding that women tend to have more poorly developed spatial abilities than men.

Knowledge of brain function continues to progress but our

understanding of the neuroanatomical and neurophysiological substrates of intellect, perception and language remain incomplete.

Further reading:

Kandel E.R. & Schwarz J.H. (1981) *Principles of Neural Sciences.*
London, Edward Arnold.
Penfield W. & Roberts L. (1959) *Speech and Brain Mechanisms.*
Princeton, N.J., Princeton University Press.

CHAPTER 8

Remembering and Forgetting

The ability to store and recall previous experiences is fundamental to effective human functioning. This recall of past events need not be conscious; many of our current activities are based upon habit, and habit itself might be considered a form of memory. Habits are acquired through the process of learning, and they are derived entirely from previous experiences. It would not be possible to read these sentences unless one could recall the skills that had been learned years earlier when at primary school. The cardinal importance of the processes of memory may only be fully appreciated if the associations and recollections of the past are brought to bear now to give this proposition meaning. The very act of thinking about the nature of memory calls into action the memory stores of the thinker.

The learning and recall of past experiences is a cognitive process that has value in enabling an individual to modify his environment. It is very difficult to imagine how one might function if one lived solely in this instant of time. Every purposeful act involves some elements of previous learning, and the consequences of the act contribute to future memory stores. There is evidence to suggest that the nervous system is permanently altered as a result of experience, and the resulting modification of behaviour controlled by the altered nervous system can be thought of as a demonstration of an aspect of memory. In practice the word *memory* is used when discussing cognitive processes and *habit* when referring to motor behaviour which has been modified through learning.

This chapter concentrates upon conscious learning, the deliberate attempt to acquire knowledge or to store information with the purpose of retaining it for reproduction at some later time.

Memory may be thought of as a measure of the effectiveness of the learning process. If something is to be learned and retained for later recall then some type of *reinforcement* must be present. With regard to cognitive learning this is commonly secondary reinforcement, for example social approval, the desire to acquire qualifications, status, money, and so on. One great advantage of cognitive learning is that the process of learning or memorizing can itself serve as a reward. A good example may be seen in learning to play the piano when the acquisition of skills to produce a musical sound, a simple tune, may well itself serve to maintain the motivation and to keep the learning going.

The act of remembering presumes previous learning, and involves at least three main steps:

(1) recognising the request to recall and preparing to search the memory files,

(2) going to the correct file, reviewing relevant memories or associations, and picking out the particular items, and

(3) reproducing the memory through some medium of communication, i.e. speech, writing, gesture and so on.

Broadly speaking, the pleasanter the original learning experience, the more readily it is remembered.

Certain extrinsic factors and instrinsic aspects of the material to be memorized affect the quality of learning:

(1) extrinsic factors
  (a) age,
  (b) intelligence,
  (c) motivation,
  (d) physical state, i.e. fatigue, cold, etc, and
  (e) stress,
(2) intrinsic factors
  (a) meaningful material,
  (b) part v whole learning,
  (c) massed v spaced practice,
  (d) interference from previous learning, and
  (e) sense modalities involved.

The act of remembering

A more detailed analysis of the act of remembering reveals that it incorporates several different aspects of the process.

Recognition

This activity results in a positive or negative response that a particular stimulus has been perceived before. It is, perhaps, the
simplest form of memory although there are many reports of false
or erroneous recognition leading to mistaken ideas or beliefs, for
example, the phenomenon of déjà vu (recognizing as already seen,
an entirely new visual perception).

Recall

This process represents an active search of stored material upon
demand. Often the recollection may be vague or generalised and
more cues are generally required before accurate recall can be
achieved. It usually involves longer term memory store where there
is a tendency to file experiences or previous learning under general
headings or *gists*. Because the acquisition of novel experience
appears to present an immense storage problem over a lifespan, *gist
learning* is reminiscent of the constancy phenomenon in the process
of perception. Essential aspects of an experience are retained and
incidentals tend to be lost from memory.

Reproduction

This calls for an accurate presentation of previously learned
material. For this to occur there usually needs to have been *overlearning*, unless the reproduction follows a very brief time interval
after the initial perception of the material. This time interval
can be so brief in some people that they cannot retain and accurately reproduce a telephone number a few seconds after reading it
in a directory. To overcome this type of problem many people
resort to repetition and rehearsal until the number is dialled where-
upon it generally vanishes from memory. On the other hand, many
people can accurately reproduce nursery rhymes, arithmetic tables,
or prayers after long periods, even years, without intervening rehearsal. An interesting aspect of reproduction is that an effort to
make the recall conscious can have the effect of blocking the
memory so the individual has to repeat the entire passage again
without thinking too much about it.

Performance memory

This is the re-enactment of previously acquired habits and is very similar to reproduction except that no language or conscious thought processes need be involved. A good example is being able to ride a bicycle after a gap of many years. This would be a situation where the stimuli present succeed in eliciting previously acquired skills that are reproduced automatically and have been retained not just from day to day but over prolonged periods.

The process of memory and recall

It is instructive to examine the process of memorizing and subsequent recall in some detail. A typical example might be a consideration of a general practitioner's advice to a patient and the likelihood of that patient being able to remember and comply with the advice.

Stage 1. Perception of the stimulus material

If anything is to be memorised the experience must first be recognised. Recognition itself involves recall in so far as it comprises associations which give the experience meaning. This is almost instantaneous and occupies a very short period of time indeed. The more unusual or complicated the material, the longer it takes for it to be recognised as a meaningful stimulus. In real life we almost never experience single isolated stimuli; they usually appear in series or chains against a background of other sensory experiences. For example, when reading a passage in a book the reader may recognise individual words and his rate of reading is determined by the time taken to recognise each word in the chain. In order to achieve a faster reading rate the lines tend to be scanned with note being taken only of occasional significant words. In such circumstances not only are background stimuli ignored but there is selective attention given to certain words on the page. Patients listening to doctors reveal similar characteristics. Certain words or signals that have particular personal meaning for the patient may be attended to and an effort made to make sense of these particular bits of information. It is obvious that the speed of presentation of stimuli is important if the material is to be recognised and retained. Of equal importance is the interference of extraneous stimuli that may be present, for instance, outside noises, frightening bits of equipment on view.

Stage 2. Short-term memory

This stage in the storage of information normally requires the material to be turned into symbols for easy filing. For adults this is usually achieved through language but intense experiences may be retained directly from the sensory store, for example the recollection of strong odours or the recall of acute disturbances of autonomic functioning during a panic attack. There is some evidence that young children are able to store detailed visual information as a kind of mental picture over quite long periods of time. This phenomenon is referred to as *eidetic imagery* and is an ability that tends to disappear as the superiority of linguistic symbols for retention becomes more apparent in adult life. It has been suggested that in some societies without a written language and with a limited vocabulary pictorial recall remains an active process.

There is a limit to the amount of material that can be held in short-term store. Quite a deal of information can be lost simply due to the continuous presentation of more material. This limit varies from person to person and also according to the type of material being held in store. In an effort to overcome this problem individuals employ various techniques like repetition, rehearsal and deliberate attempts to cut out extraneous material while retaining the *gist* or principle of what is necessary to be remembered. The ability to *encode* at a fast rate, that is to turn experiences into readily retainable symbols, enables more material to be held in short term store.

To return to the example of a general practitioner giving advice and instruction to a patient, assuming the information is comprehensible and has been presented well, the patient ought to leave the surgery with the material held in short-term store. The problem of encoding might be assisted by providing repetition of the instructions and perhaps in addition, the presentation of written material.

Stage 3. Transfer to long-term store

This final step in the memory process involves the use of symbols, usually language, when the material to be retained is filed. The permanency of the long-term store is related to the number of associations attached to the information and the amount of learning that has gone into the memorizing process. There is often a loss of material in the transfer from short-term to long-term memory so that repeated experiences are necessary if the longer-term memory is to be accurate in detail. New material that is being transferred from short-term store can interfere with the retention of previously acquired material. Almost any new experience of significance can interfere with the long-term retention of the doctor's instructions. Thus the patient may return home with only a very sketchy memory of what had been said in the surgery, and only make any conscious effort to remember the instructions when the situation demands it.

Stage 4. Retrieval from store

The way in which efforts are made to remember depends very much upon the kind of task being set. It may be a *matching task* such as when purchasing curtain material to fit in with a certain house décor, or at a police station when as a witness of some criminal act one may be invited to try and recognise a face in a book of photographs. In such circumstances matching or *recognition memory* can be very unreliable though the persons trying to carry out the task may feel quite confident of their decisions.

Reproduction of previously learned material is a form of retrieval that most students have experienced. It is often the case that the material has been memorized as a long sequence and an attempt to retrieve just a small part may entail having to go through the entire material. Practice and overlearning often improve retrieval; when an 11 year old is asked to state what are eight times seven, it should not prove necessary for the entire table to be recited, as might have happened a couple of years earlier when the initial learning took place. Generally, however, retrieval is a fairly automatic process as the stimulus material, the request to recall, serves to trigger associations and the relevant files seem to become more active and available.

Certain factors have a demonstrable effect upon retrieval, the more important of which are:

(1) The shorter the time interval between the learning and the act

of recall, the more detailed and accurate is the retrieval.

(2) The more cues or aids that are available to trigger associations, the better the recall.

(3) The less the extraneous stimulation between the efforts to memorize and the act of recall, the better the recollection. Sleep has proved to have the least effect in terms of interfering with memory, in that material learned last thing before going to sleep is well recalled hours later upon waking. This contrasts favourably with intervals of similar duration that have been filled with other types of activity.

(4) There is some evidence that in sleep, memories are put into files of some permanence where they are associated with relevant previous experiences. This process is referred to as *consolidation*, and it can be demonstrated that the storage of information is interfered with by long periods of sleeplessness.

(5) The activity of *overlearning*, that is, continuing to practice the acquisition of material by repetition long after it can be reproduced with 100% accuracy from short-term memory stores, serves to aid retrieval. For instance, a child may learn to ride a bicycle and once having acquired the skill, may go on practising for a long time. If he then should cease to engage in cycling when he grows up and buys a car, he is still able to retrieve his cycling skills many years later with little effort.

Forgetting

Finally there arises the issue of forgetting, that is, the gradual loss of memory even after the initial learning has been adequate and retention might have been expected to be relatively permanent. Simple experiments involving recall demonstrate the nature of the forgetting process. Consider a task involving learning a word list so that it can be reproduced with 100% accuracy. Attempts to recall and reproduce the list 24 hours later reveals a loss of information, and after 3 days it is likely that only about one-third of the material is retained. Further learning trials may be carried out in an effort to strengthen the memory traces and this may be repeated many times until something like permanent storage has been achieved. It is quite likely, however that despite all efforts to memorize adequately, our memories finally begin to fail us in later life.

Models of memory

Two competing theoretical models have been put forward to account for forgetting. They are a *decay theory* and an *interference theory*.

The decay theory

A somewhat naive version of the decay model has been current for at least 500 years. The belief is that as an individual ages so his memory stores begin to degenerate and a lot of material is lost, while at the same time, new learning is not retained because an adequate storage system is no longer available, and material just has to be packed into existing files where it gets lost. An analogy might be a computer system in which the data storage tapes gradually become degraded over time and no new files can be opened. Clinicians have pointed to the relationship between the degeneration of the central nervous system and evidence of failing memory. In these circumstances it is interesting to note that new learning is badly affected and there is generally poor recall of recent experiences. By contrast, old learning, memories of long past events may hardly seem to be affected at all. The forgetting process seen in the elderly seems to progress backwards such that a patient may have forgotten what happened last week no matter how significant the event, but can well remember experiences of a decade earlier.

The interference theory

The 1950s and 1960s saw a resurgence of interest in cognitive psychology and, in particular, attention was turned to the process of human learning. The advocates of the interference model argued that forgetting was due to the effect of new experiences upon old learning. They pointed to the experimental findings relating to short-term memory which demonstrate a limit to capacity, such that new information could interfere with previously acquired material. Many experiments were carried out which sought to demonstrate that forgetting was the result of interference of new learning with old and vice versa. It was suggested that childhood experiences were well remembered because the stores were large, empty and available at that time. As humans age so the stores fill up and new material is retained only after competing with existing stored information, some being lost and some retained. The interference school point to individuals claiming to have a clear recollection of some particular past event, for example as a witness of a car crash. Careful checking of these memories commonly reveals that the details are quite inaccurate and the recollection is in fact a composite event made up of many experiences derived from similar occurrences often spread over several years.

Given that there are limitations to human memory function and that humans easily forget, techniques had to be developed to help overcome this difficulty. In real-life situations it may be important not to forget something and yet it may not be possible at that time to commit it to memory using traditional memorizing methods. An obvious technique of resisting the tendency to forget is to code the information or experience in such a way as to facilitate its retention in short term store, and to cross-reference it to other files in longer term store. It has been known for some time that long term store is coded in a manner that facilitates retrieval through a system of cross-references or associations. Broadly speaking it would seem that *phonetic* similarities lead to confusion while *semantic* relationships facilitate storage and retrieval. Recent research suggests that semantic features of words are well retained even after long delays between the learning and recall. It would seem that the relationship between semantic coding and long-term memory has considerable generality. It must be emphasised that virtually all thinking uses verbal symbols, and storage systems that depend upon meanings of words would seem to be relatively resistant to forgetting. This is well demonstrated by administering intelligence tests to elderly people and observing that verbal functioning declines least compared with other abilities, even when the old person's memory is impaired.

A serious problem that occurs when trying to examine the process of forgetting is that it may not be qualities of the memory storage that are being investigated, but rather difficulties of retrieval. For example, an individual about to go on holiday to Italy may be instructed that the word for *hot* indicated on taps, is *caldo*. It is quite likely he will try the wrong tap when he wants a cold drink, and yet be able to remember quite clearly the instructions given to him before his departure. What has occurred has been an error in information retrieval possibly due to thinking habits based upon existing memory storage systems. Another example is when a person has the experience of knowing he has a memory of something but when asked to engage in the act of recall, just cannot reproduce the desired word. This is a phenomenon that may become something of a problem following certain kinds of brain damage. Words seem to 'disappear off the tongue' just before expression and communication becomes circumlocutory and vague. Yet all the time the sufferer feels he is well able to remember and in any case he can make sense of incoming information which demonstrates the availability of previous learning or memory stores.

Needless to say, there are many difficulties that can arise as a result of impaired memory function. It is a topic of particular clinical importance in the specialties of neurology and psychiatry but may indeed be a significant issue in all aspects of living. In order fully to appreciate the clinical significance of serious memory disorder and to undertake constructive action, it is imperative that the apparent poor memory be examined in detail in a systematic way. Difficulties may be experienced at any stage in the memorizing and recall process, and these problems may be due to factors associated with the material memorized, and the environment, as well as in the remembering and retrieval process.

CHAPTER 9

Sleep, Arousal and Biological Rhythms

Behaviour can be studied, both from a qualitative and from a quantitative point of view. The qualitative aspects are about what people do, and they include attempts to explain the wide variation in behaviours seen both within and between people. Much of this book is to do with the qualitative side of behavioural science, since an understanding of individual differences is of vital importance for the practice of good medicine. In this chapter, however, we are more concerned with the quantitative or intensity aspects of behaviour.

Arousal

There is a 'common-sense' continuum, labelled *behavioural arousal*, defined by sleep at one end, and extending through drowsiness and alertness, to excitement and panic at the other. Associated loosely with this variation are physiological changes, particularly an increase in sympathetic dominance within the autonomic nervous system, and a shift towards fragmented electrocortical activity with higher frequencies becoming manifest. The neurophysiological bases for these changes probably lie within the *ascending reticular activating system* (ARAS), whose integrity is necessary for efficient waking activity, and which serves to mediate between external events and internal activation. Changes in sensory input increase the activity of the ARAS; this arouses or activates the organism to deal with the associated environmental changes. Monotonous, unchanging stimuli on the other hand decrease arousal and move the organism nearer sleep, an experience well-known to students suffering a boring lecture on a Friday afternoon. Drugs that act on the central nervous system can be classified in

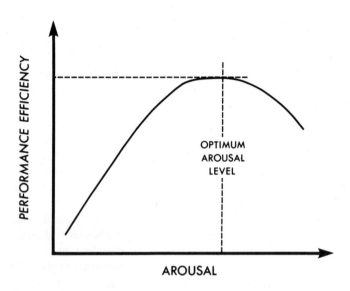

Fig. 9.1.   Yerkes–Dodson curve.

terms of their effects on arousal. Thus, stimulants such as amphe-
tamine and caffeine, increase arousal, whereas depressants like
alcohol and the tranquillisers, lower it.

There is an important relationship between the level of arousal
and the efficiency of performance on a variety of tasks. Generally
speaking, as arousal increases so also does efficiency of performance until an otpimum level is reached, beyond which, if arousal
increases still further, efficiency tends to deteriorate. This inverted-U
relationship is sometimes known as the Yerkes–Dodson curve (Fig.
9.1). The optimum level of arousal varies according to the
complexity of the task. The more complex the task, the lower the
level of arousal associated with the best performance. Thus, the
fine motor skills required for surgery are more efficiently
performed at relatively low levels of arousal, while the carving of
the Sunday roast can be attempted quite successfully at higher
levels. The deliberate but misguided use of drugs to alter arousal is
relevant here; for example, drinking black coffee (caffeine) to
combat the effects of tiredness while revising the night before an
examination; and then having a couple of pints of beer immediately

before the examination to calm oneself down. Some evidence points to the possibility that the relationship between optimum arousal and task complexity is moderated by individual differences. Thus, different people may maintain characteristically different levels of arousal, and this is reflected in their behaviour. Those who are poorly aroused seek stimulation to push their arousal towards its optimum. They may engage in *stimulus seeking*, prefer noisy environments, and tolerate, even prefer change. On the other hand, highly aroused individuals seek to maintain or to minimise the level of stimulation, and avoid change or noise as this moves them over the top of their arousal/performance curve.

Terms such as arousal, anxiety, physiological activation and stress are often used as though they were synonyms for each other. It should, however, be noted that *arousal* is an abstraction, changes in which may be manifested by changes in physiological activity, or behaviour, or anxiety. The concordance between these different aspects of arousal is not perfect, particularly within individuals, so that although the concept of arousal seems to make sense between and within individuals, its measurement in universal terms is unsatisfactory at present. Knowledge of a person's level of arousal has potential value in several areas, for example determining the job or activity that is appropriate for that person's optimum arousal level, or gauging the amount of anaesthetic a particular person requires to achieve the desired level of arousal, that is unconsciousness. There is also the advantage of having a unifying framework within which to consider various sources of information about the same person: behavioural, neurophysiological, and autonomic.

Stages of sleep

At the low end of the arousal continuum is sleep, a condition which is not static, but is characterized by a continual shifting between different states. These states for the most part reflect quantitative changes in physiological activity, particularly electrocortical changes as shown by the electroencephalogram (EEG). Four stages of sleep are conventionally defined in terms of the amplitude and frequency of the EEG. *Stage 1* sleep is defined by low amplitude signals, primarily within the frequency band 6–10 Hz, whereas *stage 4* has high amplitude 1–2 Hz activity. Stages 2 and 3 have intermediate characteristics. Autonomic activity tends to decrease as sleep changes from Stage 1 to Stage 4. The distinction between these stages is arbitrary, but there is a clear progression to a deeper sleep, in that a person in Stage 4 sleep is more difficult to rouse than when in Stage 1. Throughout the period of sleep, the depth of sleep changes in a cyclical manner. There is a fairly rapid descent into Stage 4 early in the sleep period, followed by a rise to Stage 2, then back to a deeper sleep, and up again, and so on three or four times during each night (or sleep period). The length of these cycles is about ninety minutes. More time is spent in Stage 4 in the first half of sleep than in the second half. Thus, deeper sleep occurs earlier in the sleep period.

Almost invariably, when the sleep lightens to Stage 2, another stage is entered which seems to be qualitatively different from others. Here, pulse and respiration become irregular, muscle tone decreases markedly, and the EEG is like that of the waking state, consisting of low voltage, fast frequencies. However, the most striking phenomenon of this stage is that of *rapid eye movements* (REM); indeed this stage is usually labelled REM sleep. Despite the appearance of a waking EEG pattern, REM sleep is the deepest sleep, in that the sleeper is more difficult to rouse compared with other stages. These REM periods last about fifteen to twenty minutes each, and take up approximately 20% of the total sleep time of young adults, assuming that they occur three to four times per sleep period. Neonates spend about 50% of their sleep time in REM sleep, whereas in the over 60 year olds, the proportion is reduced to 15%. REM sleep appears to be a universal phenomenon in that most species show it, but its significance is unknown. All we can say is that studies of REM deprivation indicate that REM sleep in necessary for efficient waking behaviour. Preventing people from having the other stages of sleep does not disrupt waking behaviour to the same extent as deprivation of equivalent amounts of REM sleep.

A most interesting observation regarding REM sleep in humans is that if the sleeper is wakened during a REM period, a dream is reported on average seven times out of ten. If, on the other hand, waking occurs during a non-REM period, a dream is much less likely to be reported. REM sleep is therefore also known as dreaming sleep. We can state with a high degree of confidence that everybody dreams about three times each sleep period. Not everybody, of course, recalls their dreams, and the characteristics of dream recallers compared with non-recallers have not, to date been adequately evaluated. As with REM sleep, the function of dreams is unclear. They have always fascinated mankind and a variety of explanations have been put forward, from the symbolic representation of unconscious psychic life, to the randomized sifting through of the day's events. However, at the end of the twentieth century we are no nearer an explanation of dreams than we were at the dawn of history.

Other biological cycles

A sleep–waking cycle can be identified in most species, and is perhaps the most common biological rhythm. It is, however, not too difficult to identify other rhythmic activities with varying cycle lengths; the menstrual cycle being one of the most obvious. Endogenous rhythms, have been observed in the activity of single cells, and the clearly identifiable EEG rhythms, particularly the alpha rhythm of about 10 Hz, may reflect aggregates of cells beating in unison. Given the pervasiveness of cyclical phenomena, it is not unreasonable to suppose that rhythmicity can be considered a fundamental property of biological systems, at all levels of complexity, from the cell to the whole organism. Certainly at a behavioural level we can identify changes in mood which seem to be endogenous in origin, in that they are difficult to associate with definable environmental events, and which may well follow a regular cyclical course. The amplitude and cycle length of the fluctuations, of course, varies considerably from one person to another. The dimension of mood referred to here is best described as an 'up–down' dimension, or 'happiness–sadness' or in its clinical manifestation 'mania–depression'. Manic-depressive psychosis is a condition characterized by regular cyclical mood changes, the cycle length varying from months to years. Also identified are unipolar depressive conditions which may reflect the same process, but the 'up' swing flattens out at normality so that only the depressive component is noticeable. Unipolar mania seems to be rare clinically but is probably undetected because mild degrees of mania are more socially and personally acceptable than depression.

It seems reasonable to state that no human function, whether it is cellular, physiological, biochemical, behavioural or sociological, is constant. Variation is a fundamental property of biological systems, within as well as between persons. Studies of the phenomemon of intra-individual variation may well shed light on diseases whose course waxes and wanes independently of any prescribed treatment programme, or of environmental events. The important conclusion to draw from considerations of rhythmic activity within individuals, is that for any given measure which shows variability, the variance within individuals could well be comparable to that between persons. Consequently, from a practical point of view, importance should never be placed on single values, be they physiological, biochemical or behavioural. If the variability of a measure within a particular person is not established, then the mean of a number of observations is the only safe datum on which to base conclusions.

CHAPTER 10

Emotion

Our emotions form a significant part of our total experience. Knowledge and understanding of emotions are important for the practice of good medicine since very few people remain ill without associated emotional reaction to the fact of being ill. This reaction can modify the clinical picture, or even change the course of the illness. As with many concepts in behavioural science, *emotion* is a word frequently used but difficult to define. It refers to a subjective experience, which is therefore personal and irrefutable. As in the case of pain, the doctor cannot deny the patient's report of emotional experience, even though there may be no overt, demonstrable correlates with it. If I say: 'I feel anxious', you cannot deny my emotion, even though I may not be showing all the signs that you expect with the report of *anxiety*. Emotional experiences need words to be communicated, compared and labelled, and this may lead to misunderstandings and confusion. Do the same words refer to the same experiences? This is especially relevant when a patient of limited verbal fluency attempts to describe the complexities of how they are *feeling* to a doctor whose use of words may be much more sophisticated. Considerations of this sort apply just as much to a patient's description of physical symptoms as they do to psychological symptoms. Because of these difficulties, modern usage of the term *emotion* makes reference to behavioural and physiological, as well as to verbal/psychological components.

An emotion may be defined as a relatively transient response by an individual to their perception of some change in themselves or their environment. *Appraisal* is the process by which meaning is attached to the perceived change. For example, if you are walking along a street and are suddenly confronted by a masked person pointing a gun at you, the most likely appraisal is in terms of a threat to your person. Clearly this process is determined by past experiences; if you do not know what a gun is, then you interpret the situation differently. The setting in which the change occurs is also relevant to the appraisal. If you are an actor in the above scene, in front of film cameras, the appraisal of threat is not made, provided the use of a gun has been written into the script. The appraisal process is concerned with making sense of present circumstances, usually in terms of what might happen next. The complex of events called *emotion* generally reflects the person's preparation for the anticipated future.

Somatic aspects of emotion

We can identify a number of physiological factors which are relevant to the experience and manifestation of an emotional response. Clearly the central nervous system (CNS) is involved in the appraisal process, since it is concerned with the perception and interpretation of sensory stimuli. There is also evidence that the behavioural component of an emotion, for example the aggression associated with anger, is influenced by areas of the frontal cortex. These influences appear to be mainly inhibitory. Procedures which reduce the interaction between the frontal lobes and the rest of the brain, such as pre-frontal leucotomy or the ingestion of alcohol, generally have a disinhibiting effect. The limbic system is of crucial importance to the appraisal process because of its involvement in memory functions and also because the hypothalamus controls the activities of the autonomic nervous system (ANS).

The peripheral manifestations of ANS activation, of course, comprise a major part of the physiological component of an emotion. Such common phrases as: 'blushing with shame'; 'white with rage'; and 'butterflies in the stomach'; attest to the powerful role autonomic changes, and awareness of these changes, play in emotional experience. There is also evidence for a qualitative involvement of the ANS in that the *felt* emotions of anger and fear are associated with different patterns of physiological activation. Fear is experienced with physiological changes similar to those occurring after an injection of adrenaline; while anger is associated with changes like those consequent upon an injection of adrenaline combined with noradrenaline. However, the converse of this relationship is not true: an injection of adrenaline does not necessarily lead to the experience of fear. The crucial factor in the determination of the qualitative aspects of an emotional experience seems to be the situation in which the physiological changes occur. For example, if I perspire in a warm room, I am likely to interpret the sweating as a response to the high temperature. However, if I perspire in the presence of a hungry lion, I am more likely to feel afraid rather than hot. On the other hand, if I do not sweat when confronted with a hungry lion, I am likely to feel less afraid than if I sweat profusely. Some physiological change is necessary for an emotional change to be recognised as such.

Consequently the experience of an emotion must result from an interaction between what is happening physiologically and the significance of the setting in which it is happening. The appraisal process thus uses information, not just from the external world, but also from internal activities, particularly the manifestations of autonomic activity. It is a process being continually updated in the light of new information assimilated by constant monitoring.

Emotions and learning

The importance of past experience in appraisal suggests that emotions can be learned, and the ease with which autonomic activity can be modified by classical conditioning indicates a possible mechanism for this learning. One important implication of this is that the memory of physiological and behavioural changes and their significance, provides a powerful set of cues to present emotional experience. The memory does not have to be in consciousness for the results of learning to be shown. It is possible for the activity of the ANS to be modified at an unconscious (subliminal) level, so that an emotional response can be associated with a stimulus of which the person is not aware. It can therefore also be elicited by stimuli outside present awareness leading to unexplained mood changes which may be distressing; for example, 'I am upset because I do not know why I am feeling upset'.

If the classical conditioning model is appropriate, then it should be possible to identify the unconditional stimulus–unconditional response (UCS–UCR) pairing, that is there should be some built-in appraisals to certain types of stimuli, which are universal. For obvious clinical reasons, most of the work in this area concerns the experiences of anxiety and depression. Anxiety tends to be associated with the appraisal of a situation in terms of threat, whether physical or psychological. The physiological concomitants of

anxiety clearly have biological significance with respect to preparing the person for meeting possible danger. Depression, or at
least the hopeless/helpless aspects of this complex experience,
seems to be associated with the perception of a personal loss of
control, or of mastery, over one's environment. Other emotions
such as happiness, anger and love presumably have equivalent
associations, although the evidence here is minimal, because of the
difficulty of reliably eliciting these emotions under controlled
conditions.

Emotion and disease

Given the intimate association between emotions and physiological
changes, together with the ease with which the physiological components in particular can be learned, we have the beginnings of a
rational model for *psychosomatic* disorders. This is a much-abused
term which refers to those illnesses where the maintenance or
aetiology of physical pathology seems to be associated with
emotional or psychological factors. If a person is exposed to an
altering environment, or at least one in which appraisal changes,
then according to the model outlined earlier, this person experiences changing emotions together with the physiological concomitants. If these physical changes are prolonged and intense
enough, then illness may occur. The association between illness and
life events (Chapter 20) would support this analysis. An explanation of why different people develop different illnesses under
ostensibly similar situations further strengthens this model. Such
an explanation is available in the concept of *response specificity*,
which refers to the fact that a proportion of the population (about
25%) show consistent patterning of their physiological responses to
a variety of stimuli. We can thus refer to *heart responders, muscle
responders, stomach responders*, and so on. Should a particular
individual be exposed to a number of life changes, which are
appraised in such a way as to evoke intense or prolonged emotional
responses of a similar type, and if the person is a heart responder,
the risk for an illness involving the cardiovascular system may be
increased.

The value of this model is that it indicates some possible modes
of treatment, and indeed prevention. The cycle of appraisal-
emotion–appraisal can be theoretically broken at any point. For
example, if I do not appraise the hungry lion in terms of threat, I

do not feel frightened, and I do not sweat, have palpitations, and so on. Changing the appraisal is the basis of a class of therapeutic techniques loosely called *cognitive* therapy. These may be based on a variety of theoretical models ranging from the psychodynamic to the humanistic. There is little evidence, however, that these *talking treatments* on their own, are effective. Interventions designed to modify the physiological and behavioural components of emotion appear to be relatively more successful. This is consistent with our earlier contention regarding the powerful effect physiological activation has on *psychological* phenomena such as emotions. However, the converse is also true and many of the newer techniques for the modification of physiological responses rely on the person learning an active skill of control, which is initiated by the higher psychological levels of functioning. Yoga, meditation, and relaxation all have a similar effect on physiological functioning. This effect seems to be initiated by a conscious decision on the part of the person concerned; hence the classification of these methods as techniques of *self control*.

An interesting recent variant of physiological self-control is the technique of *biofeedback*. This involves the monitoring and presentation to the subject of physiological information. Normally we are not too aware of how fast our heart is beating, but if we see this information displayed continuously on a dial or a screen, there is evidence that we can learn to control it. This method of self-control of specific physiological variables has potential in the prevention and cure of many illnessess affecting primarily one physiological system, such as hypertension.

Emotions are clearly complex, multi-determined phenomena. They reflect more than anything else the interaction at the interface between psyche and soma. A close study of their determinants illuminates many areas of medicine, since their effects are both pervasive and universal.

Further reading:

Van Toller C. (1979) *The Nervous Body*, Chichester, Wiley.
Mandler G. (1975) *Mind and Emotion*. Chichester, Wiley.

CHAPTER 11

Personality

Personality, in common with many other topics considered in this text, is a term indicating a broad, ill-defined area of the behavioural sciences. *Personality* refers to those consistencies in a person's psychological make-up that enable that person to be identified as a distinct individual, and distinguished from others. In the same way that a person is recognised by physical characteristics, he or she may also be recognised by characteristic behaviour. As a consequence we are generally surprised when another person does not behave as expected, and we say that they have acted 'out of character'. This would suggest that we believe we can predict a person's behaviour on the basis of our assessment of their *character*, or *personality*. If we say somebody has a 'sociable' personality, we expect them to behave in a particular way, differently from somebody we describe as being 'shy'.

Two broad themes are identifiable in the study of personality. The first, and most extensive is concerned with description, where attempts are made to identify and to define consistencies within people. The second theme is to do with explanation, answering the question 'Why are people consistent?' Although this second stage is clearly of considerable importance for any adequate general science of behaviour, to date it has been relatively poorly developed. Adequate explanatory models for personality are the exception rather than the rule.

Description of personality

The descriptive approach may be further subdivided into *typology* and *traitology*. Typology attempts to classify people into pigeon-holes, or types. Hippocrates described four types: the *melancholic, sanguine, choleric* and *phlegmatic*, each with a characteristic pattern of behaviour. Current diagnostic practice in psychiatry is an example of typology. In this context, diagnosis means classifying people in terms of their consistent, recent patterns of thought, feelings and behaviour. If certain characteristics are reliably observed to occur together in a number of people, they form the basis of a *type*. For example, the *intellectual* type, the *criminal* type, or to refer to Chapter 16, the *psychopathic* personality, or the *obsessional* personality.

Some authors have suggested that physique and personality are related and that certain physical types have characteristic personality. Thus, a person with an endomorphic body build (square shape with excess fat) was thought to be of a cyclothymic disposition (alternately happy and sad). On the other hand, an ectomorphic body build (narrow body, no fat) was associated with a schizoid (shy, aloof) personality. Modern research has shown, however, that there is little relationship between body build and personality in the general population. There is also no hard data to confirm the many popularly held beliefs of an association between physical and behavioural characteristics. Red-headed people do not have quicker tempers than most, fat people are not more jolly, intellectuals do not have higher brows, hairy people are not more virile and blonde women are no less intelligent than the rest of the population.

The second approach to the descriptive analysis of behaviour is concerned with traits. A trait refers to an enduring behavioural disposition or tendency, which is inherent in all of us, but to characteristically different levels. Analogous measures with respect to physique would be, for example, height, weight, and forearm length. We commonly refer to traits of anxiety, sociability, aggression, and so on. Many of these trait names, however, are similar, or refer to related behaviours, such as sociability and friendliness, and much discussion has taken place amongst trait theorists as to how many really different traits there are. That is, what is the minimum number of independent traits or dimensions we must define in order to describe adequately a significant proportion of human behaviour.

The most appropriate way to answer the question of how many independent traits there are is to use a sophisticated type of multivariate analysis on a large amount of data from representative samples of the general population. The nature of the analysis will, of course, influence the results. Eysenck, for example, prefers to use an analysis which provides fairly general high level traits. His model emphasizes two dimensions called Extraversion (*E*) and Neuroticism (*N*). On the other hand, Cattell uses a technique which gives a finer structure at a lower level. He describes sixteen dimensions which are not entirely independent of each other and which can be further analysed to give Eysenck's two factors. The descriptive model here is that of a hierarchical structure of behaviour; individual pieces of behaviour are repeated to make up habits; habits which go together make up low-level traits; low-level traits which co-vary constitute high-level traits. Other authors have suggested different models and different traits, but these are usually defined on an ad hoc basis and have little statistical validity. Often these *intuitive* traits turn out to be combinations of the more rigidly derived statistical dimensions. *Anxiety* for example, is made up of a combination of Extraversion and Neuroticism, such that high levels of *N* and low levels of *E*, are found at high levels of anxiety.

The measurement of traits is usually by paper and pencil questionnaires, completed by the subject. This technique is simple, cheap and acceptable provided there is not an excessive number of questions. The more questions there are, the more reliable the measurement, but on the other hand, the less the motivation on the part of the subject to reply truthfully. This, of course, reduces the validity of the answer. Good questionnaires strike a balance between reliability and brevity. The reliability and validity of questionnaires varies considerably from one instrument to another, but most of those currently available leave much to be desired as adequate measuring instruments. Like intelligence tests, personality questionnaires are *nomothetic* devices, where one person's results are compared to those obtained from a larger sample, presumed to be representative of the general population. Many questionnaires may be criticised for their poor, or inappropriate standardisation. This of course reduces their validity.

Reasons to account for consistent behaviour

The second approach to personality, that of explanation, involves the analysis of individual behaviour in terms of the supposed reasons for that behaviour. Often reference is made to the motives, drives and needs behind behaviour, pushing the individual into action. The implicit model here is that of man, 'the hedonist', where the goals of behaviour are the satisfaction (that is reduction) of drives or needs which subjectively are unpleasant. The learning model discussed in Chapter 4 is of this type. So too is the best known theory of behaviour, that of Freud.

Freud's model suggests that behaviour is motivated by unconscious forces, moulded by the individual's history, particularly the relationship with the parents. What a person actually does, thinks or feels is thought to be the outcome of a dynamic interaction between three *psychic systems*: the id, ego and super-ego. Any disturbance of the equilibrium between these systems, which usually arises from the id, leads to changes in the activity of the other two to counteract it. The important system for behaviour is the ego, which is partly conscious and is the only one to interface with reality. The ego uses a number of *defence mechanisms* to protect the person from unacceptable psychic pressures, usually anxiety. For example, if we *forget* to go to the dentist, one explanation is that the mechanism of *repression* has forced out of consciousness the idea of going to the dentist, so that we may avoid that potentially unpleasant experience. We have *defended* ourselves against dental anxiety, or the consequences of that anxiety. A number of alternative psychodynamic theories have been put forward since Freud's, but all of them make the fundamental assumption that behaviour is determined by forces within the individual, but outside awareness. Because of this, it is extraordinarily difficult to falsify these theories, and they have never been accepted by the scientific community. The measurement of drives and motives within this framework is also fraught with methodological problems. Traditionally *projective* techniques are used, but they have fallen into disrepute because of their very low reliability and indeterminate validity.

A somewhat separate class of explanatory models are those derived from the *humanistic* school. Authors such as Maslow and Rogers, suggest that motivation can be seen in terms of an hierarchy of needs. At the lowest level are those drives and needs to do with the maintenance of physical well-being. Once these are satisfied, the important rewards in life are concerned with psychological and social needs such as *esteem*. At the highest level, the person works towards *self-actualisation* and the attainment of *peak experiences*. The central concept of this model is that of the *self*, which can be viewed from a number of standpoints: *myself as I am, myself as others see me, my ideal self*, and so on. Personality in this context is the way the person perceives themselves, that is their *self*. Although this model has a degree of face validity, along with the psychodynamic approach it lacks scientific rigour. Consequently attempts to define the key concepts, particularly in a manner amenable to measurement, leave much to be desired. An exception is Kelly's Personal Construct Theory, and its associated measurement technique, the Repertory Grid. This attempts to define, for the individual, the characteristic ways in which he sees his world. This is a good example of an *idiographic* instrument where, to interpret the results, no appeal is made to vast standardisation data, instead the individual serves as his own reference. An approach of this nature has much to commend it considering the wide inter-subject variability observed in much biological data; for example, a heart rate of 80 beats/min may represent tachycardia for one person, and a normal resting level for another.

Biological correlates of personality

Despite the links between brain and behaviour, very few personality theorists attempt to explain behavioural consistencies in terms of physiological concepts or mechanisms. Indeed, there is a strong anti-reductionist body of opinion which holds that psychological concepts have no correlates at a physical level. The subjective experience of fear, for example, can never be explained in terms of physicochemical changes at a synaptic level, it is *purely* psychological. There are, of course, arguments for and against this view, but their relevance to medicine is debatable.

One of the best known biologically orientated personality theories is that of Eysenck, which postulates that the behavioural dimension of extraversion has as its physiological substrate, activity in a neural circuit linking the ascending reticular activating system (ARAS) with the cortex and back. Extraverts have a characteristically lower level of cortical and ARAS activity than introverts. Neuroticism, on the other hand, is underpinned by a loop comprising the ARAS and the limbic system; high levels of N being associated with raised limbic arousal. The physiological concepts of this model are at best crude, and the experimental data equivocal, but the postulates are reasonably clearly stated and lead to testable hypotheses in the accepted manner of scientific method.

Social theories of personality

The approaches to personality outlined so far imply that personality is something peculiar to each of us, and that the sources of behavioural variability lie within individuals. An alternative view, which has some validity, suggests that the environment has a more potent role to play. According to this approach, behavioural consistency, when it is observed, arises from the tendency for individuals to seek relatively restricted ranges of environments, and hence to show a restricted range of behaviours, relative to the total range theoretically available. Personality is thus not something carried around with the person, but simply reflects the situations the person characteristically is found in. These situations, presumably, are those providing the most reinforcement.

A number of experiments have shown that it is possible to modify a person's behaviour by manipulating their perceived environment. Even the subjects can be surprised, as when students playing the roles of *prisoners* and *guards* played them so well, the experimenters had to terminate the study. The concept of *roles* is important here. When we adopt a particular role, we are *allowed* to behave in particular, defined ways. For example a doctor in the role of *healer* is allowed to cut open another human being and to cause them pain. Yet the same doctor in the role of parent might be upset if their child treads on a small harmless spider. Can the tough-minded surgeon be the tender-minded parent? Is behaviour infinitely flexible or modifiable? To what extent can we take responsibility for our own behaviour? These are some of the questions which arise out of any discussion of personality, and attempts to explain consistencies in behaviour. There are no cut-and-dried answers as yet, indeed there are unlikely to be, as the questions are highly complex. However, they are important and worth thinking about. Good medicine is as much to do with the study of the context in which an illness is observed, as it is of the illness itself.

CHAPTER 12

Social Behaviour

The study of social behaviour is primarily concerned with the influence that people have on each other and with the determinants of a person's reactions in a social situation. It is important to recognize that much of behaviour reflects the influence of the immediate social environment. This is illustrated by considering just two aspects of social behaviour: *social influence* and *social perception*. Social influence is concerned with how people's attitudes and behaviour are modified by others, and social perception with the factors which determine our judgments of, and responses to, others. Both these topics have important implications for medical practice.

Social influence

Soon after birth, the young child is the target of attempts to modify his or her behaviour. For most of childhood sustained efforts are made by parents and teachers to inculcate appropriate behaviour and, later, appropriate attitudes and beliefs. The process of systematic influence is known as *socialization*. Later in life socialization continues at the hands of the peer group, or perhaps of professional colleagues. In medicine, for instance, one does not only acquire scientific knowledge but a code of conduct concerned with how to behave towards other members of the profession, and how to behave towards patients. As with most professions, entry into and continuance in medicine is dependent on following a set of social rules which, strictly speaking, have nothing to do with the application of medical knowledge.

The primary mechanisms of socialization are those of *operant conditioning* and *observational learning*. Operant conditioning, the modification of behaviour by the manipulation of rewards and punishments, has been described in Chapter 4. Observational learning, or *modelling*, involves the observation of other people's behaviour and its consequences. Seeing the rewards and punishments which accrue to other people creates expectations about the consequences for oneself. Not all models are equally effective, however. Learning may be facilitated if the model has desirable features like prestige or power, as is illustrated by the way some junior doctors tend to acquire the speech mannerisms or habits of consultants. Peer models with whom the person can identify are also often effective, again providing the model is attractive in some way.

It is possible to distinguish three levels of social influence. *Compliance* occurs when someone conforms to an influence superficially, while privately retaining a different attitude. The person may be willing to do what is suggested because of the rewards or punishments which ensue, but only because of these consequences. *Identification* occurs when we adopt the attitudes of others in order to maintain a satisfactory relationship with them. A person may think that he or she really shares those beliefs, but if the identification changes under the influence of a more important relationship, the beliefs are likely to change too. *Internalization* is the most effective form of social influence. Attitudes or beliefs become our own and are resistant to changing circumstances. Doctors spend much of their time trying to influence the attitudes and behaviour of their patients, and so need to be aware of the factors which produce both superficial compliance to, as well as internalization of, the principles of healthy living.

Factors producing compliance

Under laboratory conditions it is quite easy to get people to conform to social pressures. Subjects have judged lines to be clearly longer or shorter than they really were, and in one dramatic example continued to give increasingly more powerful electric shocks to a fellow subject who was clearly in distress. This sort of compliance typically occurs when the person making the request is of higher status than the conforming subject, when the subject is in a minority of one, and when someone else is taking responsibility for any adverse consequences of the subject's behaviour. Interestingly, these conditions may be approximated to by hierarchical professions such as medicine. Nurses and doctors low in the hierarchy are likely to comply with the decisions of more senior staff even if they believe them to be wrong. In one exercise nurses were ordered by a doctor over the telephone to administer twice the maximum recommended dosage of a drug to a patient. The doctor said he would sign the order later when he returned to the ward. Although this procedure was clearly contrary to hospital policy, twenty-one out of twenty-two nurses were ready to comply with his request.

Producing more permanent attitude change

Where considerable external pressure is brought to bear on some-one to comply, little attitude change is likely to result. Ideally the minimum pressure possible should be used, so that the person has little external justification for his or her actions. In this way the person feels that the decision to comply was at least partly taken of their own free will, and that they believed in or agreed with their actions. Another way of changing attitudes is by using persuasion. This is more effective if the person doing the persuading is per-ceived as (1) credible and possessing the necessary expertise, and (2) trustworthy, preferably having no vested interest in the outcome. The message itself is more effective if it contains clear and specific instructions rather than general advice. It should aim to be *moder-ately* discrepant from the the target person's current attitude, since if it is too similar, the discrepancy may be perceived as unimportant and ignored, while if it is too great, the message may be rejected out of hand.

Social perception

Much of our social behaviour depends on our judgments about and liking for other people, whom we may have only known for a short time. These judgments may affect, among other things, our willing-ness to help people, whether in a professional or non-professional capacity, and hence the study of attraction, as well as of helping, is particularly relevant to medicine.

Determinants of liking

As might be expected, *physical attractiveness* is very important in the early stages of what American psychologists call the 'heterosexual dating situation', but it is important in many other situations too. It has been found, for instance, that magistrates give more lenient sentences to female defendants who are considered attractive. Even at 5–6 years of age physically attractive boys and girls are more popular with their peers, and with adults too. In one experiment women were given a description of an aggressive act committed by a 7-year old, which was accompanied by a photograph of either an attractive or an unattractive child. When asked to describe the child who had committed the act, the women rated the attractive children as less generally antisocial and as less likely to be aggressive in future.

Another determinant of liking is *similarity*. Husbands and wives tend to be similar not only in religion, education and social background but also in physical characteristics like height, eye colour and attractiveness, and in psychological characteristics like intelligence. The fact that general practitioners tend to spend longer talking to middle-class than to working-class patients may reflect the influence of similarity.

The third most important factor is *familiarity*. This is illustrated by the finding that student friendships in halls of residence are strongly related to the proximity of rooms and to the frequency with which students are likely to come into contact with one another. These factors are relevant to medicine because so much of its practice involves a personal relationship between doctor and patient, and some of the quality of care is likely to depend on the liking of one for the other. Like the magistrates cited above, doctors may be more sympathetic and understanding towards physically attractive patients or those who appear most similar to themselves.

Helping behaviour

Most studies of helping or *prosocial* behaviour have been carried out with non-professionals, but some of their findings are relevant to medicine. Whether bystanders intervene to help in an emergency is related to two main factors: (1) the number of people present, and (2) the perceived cause of the problem. The more people present, the less likely anyone intervenes. This may be because the presence of others helps to define the situation as a non-emergency, or because there is a diffusion of responsibility. The perceived cause of the problem is important because the more it appears to be the victim's own fault, the less likely help is to be forthcoming. In an experiment on the New York subway in which a man collapsed and lay on the ground, help was found to arrive more quickly if the man carried a cane and appeared to be ill than if he smelt of alcohol and appeared to be drunk.

Although doctors are designated by the public as helpers they too may be affected by the perceived cause of illness. This is most likely when time or other resources are scarce, in which case they may decide to allocate more time to the 'deserving' cases who are not seen as responsible for their illness. A dramatic example of this happened in the casualty department of a New York hospital, which was often faced with trying to revive apparently lifeless bodies. Researchers noticed that the length and persistence of these attempts varied with the social status of the patient: those who were seedily dressed, or who looked like vagrants or prostitutes, received much less attention than the young and smartly dressed. Such behaviour is also likely to be demonstrated in the treatment of self-poisoning; doctors often feel hostility towards those whose illness is 'their own fault'.

Helping behaviour, like any other behaviour, varies with the situation and with our perception of it. Moreover, we all tend to underestimate the extent and power of these situational forces. Medical practice could become much more effective if doctors paid more attention to these social determinants of behaviour.

Further reading:

Hilgard E.R., Atkinson R.C. & Atkinson R.L. (1979) *Introduction to Psychology*, 7th Edition. New York, Harcourt Brace Jovanovich. See Bem D.J., Chapter 18.

CHAPTER 13

Sex and Gender

Development of gender

The biological sex of the individual is determined by the Y chromosome; if it is present the primordial gonadal tissue of the embyro differentiates into testes, and their secretions in turn lead to the development of secondary sexual organs of the male. In the absence of the Y chromosome the gonadal tissue becomes ovaries and the fetal development is female.

At its birth the child is declared to be a boy or a girl, the appropriate colour, blue or pink, is chosen and throughout the life of the individual his (or her) sex influences the attitudes of others toward him. These attitudes and expectations are incorporated into his *core gender identity*, that is his (her) sense of maleness (femaleness). On occasions biological sex and the individual's core gender identity are incongruous. The most important influences on the child for developing core gender identity are the parents who, in countless ways, reinforce the child's sense of distinction between the sexes. Parents inevitably fulfil this important function in the child's life even if they protest that they treat boy and girl children 'exactly alike'. At the most obvious level girls are given dolls and encouraged to dress them in clothes, tell them stories, comb their hair and put them to bed; disapproval is shown if a girl sets two dolls in combat with one another. The opposite is the case with boys, who are also given dolls, but these are male, belong to the race of Action Man, are clad in military uniforms and are expected to fight, to be brave or to be adventurous. If the boy persistently kisses his Action Man and combs his hair then he will probably be encouraged to play with toys of a different sort.

In the playground, as in the nursery, there are boys' games and girls' games, and the sex of the child is further emphasized by styles of dress and hair length. Exhortations, subtle and not so subtle, continually serve to reinforce the child's gender identity by the encouragement of modelling on some older or admired person. The little boy is encouraged to eat his porridge so that he may 'grow up big and strong' and the phrase 'like Daddy' may be added unless Daddy happens to be an alcoholic who becomes violent in his cups or possesses other attributes of character which are not to be emulated. As the child grows he is introduced to broad differences between stereotypes of masculine and feminine behaviour, and this is still true today even though a diminishing number of occupations are the exclusive preserves of either men or women. The girl child is encouraged to learn to cook and sew while the boy makes models and is informed that he is a clever chap when he mends a puncture in his bicycle tyre. Boys' games generally incorporate more aggressive and competitive activity and the boy who dislikes such games may be called a sissy or some other derogatory term with cross-gender implications. A child's preference for the mannerisms and activities attributed to one or other of the sexes is called *gender role behaviour* and this is generally, but not always, congruent with biological sex.

Some theorists argue that the determination of a child's core gender identity is almost exclusively the responsibility of the parents and that if one or other parent rejects, or is uncomfortable with, his or her own gender assignment then, by various overt and covert influences the seeds of *gender confusion* (or gender dysphoria) will be sown in the child. However, although the parents do play an important role, the child is open to many other influences both inside and outside the home. He or she is likely to admire, and attempt to emulate, slightly older children and may rapidly identify with characters in comic magazines and television. It is unlikely that the child's developing gender identity is seriously impaired if the stereotyped sex roles of the parents are reversed and the mother goes out to work while the father stays at home to run the kitchen and the nursery.

Core gender identity is usually firmly established by the age of 3 years. The next major development in the psychosexual life of the child is that of *sexual attachment*. From innumerable sources, the most important of which is likely to be the quality of the relationships between his parents, ideas are formed concerning the nature of sexual relationships. Personality traits, and especially social confidence, contribute strongly toward developing confidence in sexual relationships. Other important and inevitably adverse influences are strong feelings of shame about sexual expression, together with an ignorance of sexual differences. The child may have been well prepared for the profound changes of puberty and informed about such matters as contraception and sexually transmitted diseases; or the reverse may be the case and the whole subject of sexual relationships may become a profound and perhaps lasting source of anxiety and misery.

Human psychosexual development is subject to gross cultural and subcultural influences. In Western societies there has been a considerable change in sexual mores since the advent of universal contraception and the concept that sexual intercourse is permissible for pleasure as well as procreation. In her classic work, the social anthropologist Margaret Mead found that in New Guinea there were large tribal differences; the Arapesh do not hold the concept of the male as the dominant partner and in another tribe, the Tchambuli, it is the women who are assertive and take over the practical management of affairs whilst the men carve and paint and practise dance steps.

The sexual response

Sexual attraction is usually toward the opposite sex. In women, as in men, the sexual response consists of four phases, and the recognition of these has clarified our understanding of sexual dysfunction. The four phases are: *arousal, plateau, orgasm* and *resolution*. During the first phase erotic feelings in relation to the partner are aroused and vaginal moistening occurs in the woman. The plateau phase may also be called the vasocongestive stage, for in the woman the labia become engorged, while in the man the corpora cavernosa are distended with blood and produce erection of the penis. This phase is largely under the neural control of the parasympathetic division of the autonomic nervous system, but is also subject to conscious control and may be prolonged at will in order to increase sexual pleasure. However, at a certain stage, ejaculation, innervated by the sympathetic division of the autonomic nervous system, inevitably occurs with secretion of seminal fluid by the prostate and seminal vesicles.

In the woman orgasm is transmitted from the clitoris and results in general bodily myotonia and spasmodic rhythmic contractions of the muscles surrounding the lower part of the vagina. In the man the orgasmic phase is characterized by a series of contractions of the muscles surrounding the root of the penis which result in ejaculation of the seminal fluid. Although the woman may be capable of experiencing repeated orgasms during a single intercourse, the man's orgasm is followed by a phase of resolution when no further genital sexual activity can occur.

In both men and women sexual responsiveness may be maintained until old age, although there is usually some decrease in arousability and, as age advances, the strength of the orgasmic phase diminishes. The woman's sexual responsiveness is not dependent upon oestrogen and is therefore not affected by her menopause. In fact the 'hormone of libido', both in men and women is testosterone, the woman's sexual responsiveness only fails if her own production of this hormone is surgically eliminated by adrenalectomy and oopherectomy, or if an antiandrogen drug, such as cyproterone acetate, is administered.

Chromosomes, intersex and hermaphroditism

Non-disjunction of the sex chromosomes may lead to a variety of abnormalities on fertilization of the ovum. Surprisingly there is usually no gross abnormality of psychosexual development, but since many of these genetic anomalies, such as the XXX syndrome, are accompanied by a general retardation of mental development it is not always possible to be sure about the individual's sexual attitudes. In the condition known as Klinefelter's syndrome the man possesses an extra X chromosome (XXY). However, the concomitant supernumary X chromosome does not lead to any specific abnormality of sexual attitude; such a person may show normal sexual behaviour or any of the varied sexual psychopathologies. Generally individuals with gender confusion do not have any abnormality of chromosomal constitution.

Faults in the programming of embryonic development may result in what is variously known as *hermaphroditism* or *intersexuality*. In hermaphroditism there is the presence of both ovarian and testicular tissue whereas in *pseudohermaphroditism* only one type of gonadal tissue is present but the individual has ambiguous internal and/or external reproductive organs. In order to be masculinized the fetal gonad must produce both mullerian-inhibiting substance and testosterone. Failure of the former results in a male fetus in whom the mullerian ducts have proceeded to differentiate into a uterus and fallopian tubes. Testosterone leads to the development of the genital tubercle into a penis and scrotum. In the *adreno-genital syndrome* the female fetus produces excess testosterone and is born with an enlarged clitoris and empty scrotum. The male counterpart of this defect is the *androgen insensitivity syndrome* in which a genetic defect blocks the uptake of androgen by target organs resulting in feminization of affected males. When such major errors affect the development of genital organs the anomaly is obvious at birth but little is known about the effects of prenatal exposure of brain tissue, in particular in the hypothalamic region, on the later development of psychosexual attitudes. There have been reports that the female offspring of rhesus monkeys who have been exposed to externally administered androgen at the fetal stage, show more male-like behaviour, preferring aggressive play and sexual mounting behaviour. There have also been sporadic reports of gender confusion occurring in the children of mothers who have been administered certain hormonal substances, for therapeutic reasons, during their pregnancies. All that can be said at present is that the possibility cannot be ignored that prenatal biogenic influences may play a part in the aetiology of some individuals who develop anomalous sexual attitudes.

Deviation of sexual preference and gender identity

The most thorough study of sexual attitudes was conducted in the USA in the 1950s by Kinsey, Pomeroy and Martin. In the case of male homosexual orientation they found that this was not an 'all or nothing' phenomenon but that some men (about 4%) were exclusively homosexual, a rather larger proportion exclusively heterosexual, whilst the majority of men had enjoyed fantasies and/or actual practice of both types at various times in their lives. Similar findings applied to women. Despite its considerable methodological difficulties, Kinsey's reports are probably valid and have done much to break down the prevalent condemnatory attitudes toward people with homosexual preferences.

Most people with fully established homosexual orientation have no gender confusion. The homosexual man does not doubt that he is male, nor does he wish to be female. Furthermore he does not usually become aware that his attitudes deviate from those of the majority until the time of puberty or later.

The most fully-established defect of core gender identity is *transsexualism*. These people, whether male or female, hold a persistent, unvarying feeling that somehow they have been born into the wrong sex. For instance the transsexual man, from his childhood on, only feels at ease if he is dressed as a woman and engaged in feminine activities; he loathes his penis and may try, in a futile manner, to avoid the constant reminder of its presence by urinating in the sitting position. He may or may not be overtly homosexual but if his preference for sexual partner is female then, during sexual intercourse, he indulges a fantasy that he is being penetrated by a penis. Most transsexual people wish for gender change. Since the first such procedure was carried out in the early 1950s an increasing number of people have taken the difficult road towards gender change, via change of name and documentation, social skills training, the administration of hormones, and finally surgical intervention. Follow-up studies have shown that, released from the tortured existence of total gender confusion, the majority of transsexuals lead happier lives after gender change.

Like homosexuality, the phenomenon of transsexualism may not be an 'all or nothing' matter. It is probable that many girls, who had marked tomboy characteristics as children, reach maturity without major gender confusion, and the same probably applies to boys with marked boyhood femininity. Then there are people who feel happy and content when they are dressed in the clothes of the opposite sex but who do not feel strongly that they should have belonged to the opposite sex or wish to proceed to gender change. These people form one group of the phenomenon of transvestism, or cross-dressing.

Little is known for certain about the causation of homosexuality and gender confusion. All too often 'homosexuals' have been considered, for the purpose of some research endeavour, as if they represented a single, defined and relatively homogeneous population, whereas it is more likely that homosexual preference is the outcome of a wide variety of biological and psychological influences. There is some evidence for a genetic factor in homosexuality, albeit not a strong one, and it may prove to be non-specific, such as a trait of personality rather than homosexuality itself. The possibility of some prenatal hormonal exposure in both homosexuality and gender confusion has been alluded to above and can as yet, not be discounted.

Most researchers have favoured a psychological explanation in the genesis of these conditions and claim to have found it. The usual scenario, supported by many research publications, is that the homosexual male is reared by a dominant, possessive mother whilst the father is aloof, absent, or in some respect does not provide a suitable model of masculinity. The problem with studies of this kind is that they are retrospective and therefore subject to the pitfalls of falsification of recall. Moreover parental attitudes may, to some extent, be determined by abnormality in the child rather than the reverse; for instance the father may be repelled by a son with feminine characteristics and therefore be more likely to absent himself from home. However, there can be little doubt that early learning experiences may lead to enduring attitudes and personality characteristics and that these in turn may facilitate or inhibit normal psychosexual development. Moreover in the case of homosexuality, as Kinsey and his colleagues showed, many people may be homosexually aroused in one period of their lives and not in another. Homosexual practice becomes very common in people confined for long periods of time to single sex institutions such as prisons or battleships.

Sexual dysfunction

This term is reserved for difficulties which arise in heterosexual intercourse. The old-fashioned terms *impotence* and *frigidity* are being replaced by more precise terms, for instance *erectile dysfunction* and *premature ejaculation* in the male, or *anorgasmia* and *vaginismus* in the female; these lead to more precise understanding and rational therapy. While the many factors that enter into the genesis of sexual dysfunction cannot be reviewed here, it is clear that anxiety concerning the sexual relationship and about sexual performance itself is most frequently implicated. Physical disease processes causing dysfunction are uncommon, although localized neuritis is probably the basis of erectile dysfunction in diabetics. Drugs may also affect the sexual response, the most common of these being alcohol and drugs with a strong sedative effect which diminish arousal. More specific drugs may interfere with one aspect of the sexual response alone, for example, drugs used in the treatment of hypertension may, through adrenergic blockade, cause failure of the orgasmic phase and consequent lack of ejaculation.

Other sexual deviation

Space precludes consideration of the phenomenal range of deviant sexual practices which may occur in both heterosexual and homosexual people. Many of these are based upon psychological factors which have led to a fear of mature heterosexual intercourse. The individual finds that he is irresistably sexually attracted to, say, children (*paedophilia*), animals (*bestiality*) or even dead people (*necrophilia*). Another common group of deviant practices depends on the need for the presence of an inanimate releasing factor for the facilitation of the sexual response; these are the so-called *fetishisms*. Fetish objects are of an infinite variety, but most commonly are materials capable of being incorporated into clothing such as fur, velvet, rubber or perhaps female garments in their entirety. Sexual deviations are largely confined to the male. Other deviant practices, such as *sado-masochism* may be in part fetishistic and in part a learned method of relationship which enhances sexual behaviour.

Further reading:

Masters W.H. & Johnson V.E. (1966) *The Human Sexual Response*. Boston, Little, Brown.
Money J. & Erhardt A. (1972) *Man and Woman, Boy and Girl*. Baltimore, John Hopkins University Press

CHAPTER 14

Families and Family Processes

The family, in the sense of a closely related group of people who live together co-operatively, is a universal human institution with a variety of crucial social functions. Family members provide each other with food, clothing and shelter; care for each other in times of distress; rear and socialize children, and in so doing establish intense and mutually supportive relationships between each other. Despite its universality as a social institution, families vary enormously in their size, membership, and in the content of relationships within them.

Membership

Conventions and expectations about who is, and who is not a member of the family vary quite dramatically from culture to culture. In the British tradition it is expected that newly married's should establish a new household, and that this should precede the birth of children. This type of family is termed *nuclear*, and is based on a tight and exclusive conjugal partnership, which ideally is permanent. Parents are responsible for their children until they reach adulthood (currently somewhere in their mid-teens). When the children establish a conjugal partnership of their own, they are expected to leave home and set up their own household.

However normal this may seem, this is but one of many ways of organizing the family. In many societies sons are expected to continue to live jointly with their fathers, and to incorporate their wives into an *extended* family. In others, ties between mother and daughter may form the core of family units, while in matrilineal societies the line of inheritance is from mother's brother to sister's son.

Role relations within the family

Motherhood, fatherhood, childhood and so forth are all *social* roles. Although influenced by the constraints of biology, they are essentially culturally organized, and so strongly influenced by the wider rules of family membership. For example, in an extended family marriage involves much more than a union between two individuals. Since a woman joins the whole of her husband's family, she may have to put as much effort into establishing good relations with her mother-in-law as with her husband. Since the marriage involves a whole group of people, both families are likely to be involved in arranging the match. In nuclear families, by constrast, marriage is more likely to be a matter of personal choice, and the conjugal partnership more intense.

Even within one general cultural system, role expectations can both change and vary enormously. For instance in Britain many husbands now play a much larger part in running the household and in childcare than was generally the case two generations ago. This change has been partly precipitated by the fact that a much larger number of women now go out to work. Styles of child-rearing, as well as the behaviour expected of children have also changed enormously, though by no means to produce a single uniform pattern. There are still major variations across regions, classes and communities.

There is no objective way in which any particular system of role relationships or expectations can be adjuged 'better' than any other, for each has its own strengths and weaknesses. Care must be taken not to make quite unjustified value judgements. One's own expectations about the appropriate way to organize family relationships will not coincide with those of all patients. Difference does not necessarily indicate deficiency, nor is the unexpected inevitably pathological. Before attempting to make any judgements it is essential to understand the norms and expectations in terms of which particular patients and their families are seeking to organize their lives, and so the resources available to them in their particular case.

Conflict

As in other small groups conflict and tension is invariably found as well as co-operation and understanding, and indeed without it family life would be exceedingly dull. Usually positive forces out-weigh the negative ones, but crises occur when they cease to do so. Members of the family then have to struggle towards a renegotiation of relationships and a new equilibrium. They may need assistance in doing so, but if this is not available, or if disagreement is so strong as to be insoluble, complete breakdown may occur. Some members may find themselves isolated and without support, while others may find themselves overburdened with responsibility, particularly for children. Such breakdowns can occur in families of all kinds, and the resulting distress can exacerbate, maintain, or even precipitate illness.

Changes in family structure

Families are not static institutions. They change over time as parents age, as children grow up, and as cultural norms alter. The precise way in which these processes work out depends upon the particular cultural and sub-cultural context. In patrilineal extended families sons grow up and begin to challenge their fathers' power, though they do not necessarily consider leaving home. In British families children usually establish independent households of their own as soon as they achieve a stable conjugal partnership. Most couples in contemporary Britain can now expect to spend a longer period of time together on their own than they did during the years of childbearing. This avoids some potential conflict between the generations, but leaves older people feeling lonely and isolated.

Figures from the Office of Population, Censuses and Surveys indicate that in 1980 only 32% of all households in Britain actually conformed to the Western stereotype of husband, wife and dependent children. A further 27% of all households were made up of married couples either with no children at all, or with children who were financially independent. 8% of all households were headed by a single parent, while a further 22% contained a single person living along. These figures are best understood in the light of demographic changes, particularly the reduction in the mean number of children born to each mother, the increase in life expectancy, and the soaring divorce rates of recent years.

From a medical perspective an important consequence of recent increases in life expectancy has been the rise in the number of elderly people living alone (See Chapter 22). In most cases the children of bereaved elderly people are themselves reaching retiring age. The kinship resources of elderly people, who constitute a large proportion of hospital in-patients, may thus be even more limited than their finances.

Illegitimacy and marital breakdown

At the other end of the age spectrum, 11% of all live births in Britain during 1980 took place outside marriage. For mothers aged under 20, 42% of all births took place outside marriage, and a further 30% were conceived premaritally. Early marriages are much more likely to end in divorce, but even so nearly one-third of all current marriages end in this way. When divorce does occur, one partner is likely to be left with sole responsibility for the children, often in extremely difficult financial circumstances. However, about one-half of those who divorce remarry within 5 years.

The illegitimacy rates of English born, Caribbean born and South Asian born mothers in the United Kingdom are respectively 11%, 51% and 1%. One way of interpreting these differences is to conclude that English families are more *broken down* than Asian, while Afro-Caribbean families are exceedingly so. Another way is to conclude that we are dealing here with different *kinds* of family organization. The latter view has much to recommend it, and the details of the argument are instructive.

In many, though not all, Afro-Caribbean families it is the relationship between mother and daughter, rather than the conjugal partnership, which provides the core of family continuity. Girls often become sexually active at an early age, and the birth of children is generally welcomed by all. There is no expectation that the girl's partnership with the child's father should necessarily be permanent, nor that he should take the responsibility for the consequences of their union. However, paternity is invariably publicly acknowledged, very often at an elaborate christening ceremony, even though lack of marriage renders the child illegitimate. In a tradition where it is grandmothers who expect to be the principal organizers of family coherence, such a state of affairs is neither puzzling nor inherently problematic. Provided there are strong ties between grandmother, mother and her children, the weakness of the conjugal tie is immaterial. Effective family support need not rest solely on marriage.

What though of Asian families? Here the illegitimacy rate is very low, as is divorce, primarily because marriage is within a wider kinship network. In consequence when things go wrong, the results can be disastrous. A failed marriage or an illegitimate birth may lead to the whole family feeling that it has been dishonoured and that the only possible response is to exclude the offender entirely from the family. Tight networks may mean that divorce and illegitimacy are much less frequent than in the English case, but also that their consequences are more devastating.

Although the significance of cultural variation can most easily be highlighted with respect to distinct minority groups such as Afro-Caribbeans and South Asians, the broad proposition which has been advanced here has a much more general application. Britain's indigenous population is, in fact, far from homogeneous. Indeed to follow through the example cited here, in some English families an illegitimate birth would cause a horrified reaction, in others mild concern, while in others it might merit no comment at all. There are no absolutes here. Events, particularly family events, must always be understood in their relevant cultural context.

Breakdown in family ties

It is worth remembering that the impending demise of family life has been confidently predicted ever since the beginning of recorded history, and yet the institution is very much with us. Change is invariably mistaken for decay.

Virtually everywhere in the industrialized world, the strength of kinship networks *between* families – involving uncles, aunts, cousins and so forth – has been greatly attenuated in recent years. Even so this attenuation is not universal. In close-knit rural communities, and in those few working class communities whose structure has not been destroyed by urban redevelopment, these networks still remain. Ties between mother and daughter, even though they live in separate households, are most noticeably resilient. However, for much of the population private leisure focussed on the television, heavy ideological stress on the value of individuality and independence, and above all geographical mobility in search of better jobs and housing has eroded many long-established patterns. Yet is is striking that Britain's many ethnic minorities have so far largely resisted this trend, and that they have largely preserved the extensive kinship networks so characteristic of English working class life in the last century.

Where these networks have been eroded, individuals and families will have much more limited external resources upon which to call in times of difficulty than was the case in the recent past. Doctors should not only check the assumptions about 'the family' in terms of which each of their patients is operating, but also what resources are actually available to them. The 'community' does not provide support if local networks do not exist, nor if they have been eroded to insignificance.

The future

Despite all the problems they may face, families are likely to sustain themselves as resilient institutions because of the vital functions they fulfil. It is into families that we are born; it is here that we are socialized, and establish our closest, most enduring and most passionate relationships. Important as our other activities may seem, it is in the domestic context that we spend the greater part of our time, that we eat and sleep and take our leisure. Above all the family is a refuge in times of stress. It is ties of family and kinship, however they may be structured, which invariably provide the soundest and most satisfying foundations for mutual support. It is for this reason that doctors need to develop the capacity to understand, and to work positively with, their patients in their domestic context, whatever shape or form their families may have.

Further reading:

Rapaport R.H., Fogarty M.P. & Rapaport R. (Eds.) (1982) *Families in Britain*. London, Routledge and Kegan Paul.

CHAPTER 15

Pain

Pain is a very complex phenomenon, a comprehensive definition of which would read: 'Pain is an unpleasant sensory and emotional experience associated with actual or potential tissue damage, or is described in terms of such damage'.

It is important to realize that pain is not a simple sensation, nor a primary perceptual experience such as hearing, smell or touch, but necessarily incudes an unpleasant emotional experience. In the words of Spinoza, it is 'a localized form of sorrow'. To investigate pain clinically, the doctor must rely upon the patient's self-report, which is influenced by emotion.

Neurophysiology

Peripheral System

Pain arises as a result of stimulation of specialized receptors, *nociceptors*, or their afferent fibres. The peripheral nociceptive system is large, comprising about 50% of the sensory fibres in a peripheral nerve. The receptors occur in two forms:

(1) the interstitial receptors, which form an unmyelinated plexus throughout the tissues, responding to local physical and chemical changes, and

(2) the perivascular network which is again unmyelinated, occurring in the walls of all blood vessels except capillaries. This network which also responds to local physical and chemical changes is not found within the central nervous system.

All human peripheral nociceptive fibres are small, less than 5 mm in diameter. The smallest 'C' fibres are unmyelinated, less than

2 mm in diameter, and are probably responsible for *dull* pain. The larger 'A' and Delta fibres, between 2–5 mm diameter, carry sensations associated with *sharp* pain.

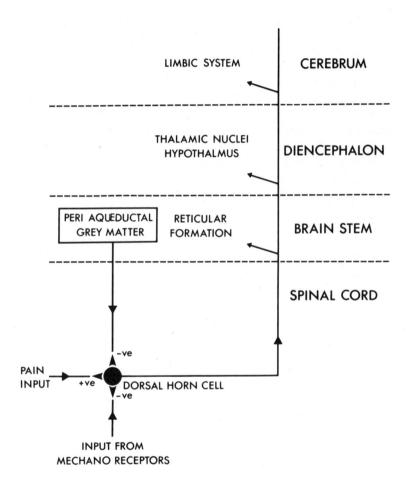

FIG. 15.1.   Pain pathways.

Central nervous system

The role of the central nervous system in processing painful stimuli is much more complex than that of the peripheral nervous system.

There are no specific pain centres in the cerebral cortex comparable with the spatially orientated projections of other sensory systems onto the cortex.

The A, Delta, and C fibres which carry the noxious stimuli enter the spinal cord segmentally in the anterior rami of the dorsal roots (See Fig. 15.1). They may give off intermediate collaterals which ascend and descend to other segments where they synapse with neurones involved with reflex and autonomic responses.

After entering the spinal cord the sensory afferents synapse with neurones in the dorsal horns of the grey matter. The cells of the dorsal horns give access to ascending tracts in the anterolateral funiculus in which pain information ascends, giving inputs on the way up to the brain stem, the reticular formation, the thalamus, hypothalamus and limbic system. This provides the central basis both for pain perception and pain-related behaviours.

Inputs to ascending pathways are controlled at the level of the dorsal horn cells. The activities of these cells can be modulated by further inhibitory inputs acting on them:

(1) *Gate theory*. Inhibition of the dorsal horn cell activity by con-current action of low-threshold mechanoreceptors synapsing with the dorsal horn cells. This is perhaps the basis for pain relief produced by massage, counter irritation techniques, and perhaps acupunture.

(2) Modulation of dorsal horn neurones by descending inhibitory pathways from higher centres, principally the brain stem peri-aqueductal grey matter. Electrical stimulation of these brain stem areas inhibits the spinal cord and produces analgesia. *Opiate transmitters* are probably involved in this system.

(3) *Serotonin (5 HT)* seems to act as an inhibitory transmitter in some descending neurones which influence the dorsal horn cells.

Psychological and social mechanisms

Pain is not a single specific sensation, but consists of several complex experiences. Different types of pain have their own unique qualities, for instance, the pain of a burn is different to that of toothache or earache, or to that of a coronary artery occlusion. Apart from the sensory aspects, pain has a variety of motivational and affective aspects; injuries which fail to produce an associated negative affect do not produce pain. Conversely the affective component of pain without sensory input, for instance the 'pain' of bereavement, is not truly pain.

Pain thresholds

There are two pain thresholds; the lower one marks the point at which a stimulus changes in nature and is first perceived as a pain. The higher threshold marks the point beyond which the pain can no longer be tolerated.

The lower threshold is fairly stable in an individual over time, but the upper threshold is much more variable, being strongly influenced by cultural and environmental factors, personality characteristics, and the meaning and significance of the pain to the individual. For example, pain tolerance may be increased in secure 'safe' surroundings, whereas it may be considerably lower in situations which are threatening, causing feelings of fear and anxiety.

Personality and pain

Not everyone complains to the same extent; some individuals of a stoical nature may suffer considerable discomfort without complaint. Various attempts have been made to measure these individual differences, especially by relating them to such dimensions of personality as Neuroticism and Extraversion described by Eysenck (see Chapter 11). In general, those who have raised Neuroticism scores report more pain with an equivalent degree of stimulation than those with lower scores. It should be noted that levels of Neuroticism tend to rise during illness, especially where pain is a feature, the levels falling as recovery begins and pain is relieved.

Individuals with high Extraversion scores are more likely to express their pain and distress than those with lower scores under similar circumstances. This can be shown in a clinical setting by looking at the amount of postoperative analgesic required, extraverts requesting more than introverts. It is important to emphasize that these personality factors may only affect the way in which the pain experience is communicated to others, rather than affecting the actual experience of pain.

Other personality traits may have an effect upon the presentation of a patient in pain, especially when traits such as obsessionality, hypochondriasis and hysteria are dominant.

Psychiatric aspects of pain

Pain is a relatively common symptom in psychiatric patients; studies have shown that between one-third and one-half of psychiatric patients have pain as one of their complaints. As a symptom, without a physical diagnosis pain is more common in female than male patients, and the presence of pain is commonly associated with a diagnosis of depression, anxiety state or personality disorder. Pain in certain areas of the body is frequently associated with psychiatric abnormality, for example low back pain and headache with anxiety states, and facial pain with depression. There are several possible explanations for this association. It has been suggested that the pain has a physical origin, and those of an anxious predisposition are more likely to complain of pain; or that the prolonged experience of pain and discomfort wears the individual down, and eventually produces secondary emotional changes.

There is a similarity between the physical signs of acute pain and an anxiety state, for instance, increased heart rate, sweating, dilated pupils, hyperventilation and hyperactivity. Some of the accompanying signs of chronic pain on the other hand are also characteristic of depression: sleep disturbance, irritability, poor appetite, retardation and social withdrawal.

Psychoanalytic workers have suggested that pain may have a role in maintaining *psychic equilibrium* with the environment, for example, in manipulating other people, expressing anger or hostility, or coping with guilt feelings.

Social aspects of pain

After suffering chronic pain over long periods of time, the patterns of behaviour gradually alter, with *pain behaviours* replacing the *well behaviours* of everyday life. The behaviour of other family members may alter also, and household routines come to revolve around the needs of the individual complaining of pain. Changes in role and status occur, often as a result of medical advice such as 'rest and take it easy', or 'try not to do anything to make it worse'. It then becomes very difficult for the patient or anyone else in the family to break these new routines, and the pain behaviours are established.

Learning also plays a part in the development and maintenance of pain behaviour. The *model* of the behaviour of other people seen in pain may influence the subject's own pain behaviour later. The early experiences of family members in pain and how they reacted to it, even the site and the type of pain, may mould the child's reaction to pain in later life. Non-organic or *psychogenic* pains frequently occur at the site of a previous physical pain; this may cause considerable diagnostic confusion. The modification of pain behaviour follows the same principles as the modification of any other learned behaviour pattern.

CHAPTER 16

Abnormal Personality and Illness

The discussion of personality in Chapter 11 highlighted the diffi-culties in the use of the term and in quantifying the relevant aspects of behaviour. Further, several of the measures of personality attri-butes described in Chapter 11, although having high statistical re-liability have little application clinically; that is, they may not give the clinician information that is useful in making decisions and planning the management of his patients' problems. On the other hand, descriptive categories of abnormal personality have been developed over a long period of time. These are often felt to be useful predictively in clinical practice, but they have the great dis-advantage that they are extremely vague and make rather unsatis-factory research criteria; statistical tests have only indicated mar-ginally significant levels of reliability. These clinical categories make explicit the way we assess other people's personality in every-day life. By observing his patient's manifestations of personality and consistent behaviour patterns, the doctor obtains useful in-formation which may help him in knowing how his patient might react to the disability of his illness and to the requirements of treat-ment. For example, when the doctor decides his patient is *obses-sional* he can give the advice that the tablets should be taken three times a day precisely half an hour before meals, and know that the patient will carry this out to the letter.

In this chapter the conventional clinical descriptions of persona-lity disorder are described, not because they are ideal or fully validated scientifically, but because they are in general use and it is helpful for the clinician to have a uniform way of describing be-haviour. A doctor who regularly observes his patients' personality with meticulous detail and thoroughness may find such criteria broadly helpful, and his assessment of personality will make him a better doctor.

Personality and abnormal personality

Personality may be assessed both from the subjective and the objective point of view. Subjectively, personality is how the patient regards himself as a unique individual; his feelings, aims and personal goals. Objectively, personality is manifested as the consistent pattern of behaviours of an individual person; it is what makes him different in his actions from other people. This implies that his behaviour will continue to be consistent (even if only that he is consistently unpredictable and chaotic), and it is for this reason that personality assessment may be useful predictively. Personality includes prevailing mood, attitudes and ways of thinking. It is manifested particularly in social interactions, in what people actually do when they are with others. The way we can most easily assess how the patient's personality manifests itself is in the exchanges between patient and doctor, although we should always ask a relative what the patient is like as well. We should also remember that the way a patient behaves with a doctor is a function of the doctor's behaviour as well as of the patient's personality.

When discussing normal and abnormal personality we are using the word 'normal' in a statistical, and not a value judgement sense. Thus, in the same way that blood sugar is 'normally' within a certain range, and it is equally abnormal to have a very high or a very low blood sugar, so personality characteristics are regarded as 'normal' within certain limits. Very much more or very much less than normal of a personality attribute like 'conscientiousness' is equally abnormal, although of course one extreme may be more acceptable than the other.

In this typological assessment of personality one looks for certain traits or categories and assesses whether they are present to a normal degree or not. One list of traits is found in the *International Classification of Diseases* (9th Revision, 1977) and forms the basis for the rest of this chapter. These personality traits should not be thought of as entirely discrete, the terms used are descriptive and impressionistic, and they are not mutually exclusive. So it is possible, for example, both to be obsessional and hysterical in personality.

Different aspects of personality and their relevance in patient care

Paranoid personality

Such people misinterpret both the words and actions of others, believing them to have special significance and to be directed against themselves. They are suspicious of other people and feel that others are antagonistic. They may be active, quarrelsome and vindictive, always ready to go to law or planning revenge, or they may be passively paranoid believing that other people wish them harm but this they just accept with resignation.

In a health context, the person with an active paranoid personality is frequently the trouble-maker on the ward; the militant campaigner for patients' rights against the better judgement of other patients who are more concerned with recovery. Of course such people are often useful in pointing out genuine examples of poor practice, and doctors do well to take notice of their grievances. The person with the more passive type of paranoid personality assumes that any complications that can occur with his particular illness will undoubtedly happen to him. His attitude of resignation makes him a 'good patient' for the staff to look after; however, he is less likely than others to take vigorous steps towards his own rehabilitation.

Affective personality

These are people who show persistent abnormality of mood as a life-long trait and not just as a temporary state or illness. Affective personality may be manifested as consistent anxiety or depression, or alternatively as excessive swings of mood from profound dejection to unreasonable euphoria, this is a cyclothymic personality. The anxious personality is frequently seen; such a person's friends and relatives know him to be a very anxious person. However, when he becomes ill and needs hospital treatment, for example an operation, he becomes much more intensely anxious. His prevailing trait of anxiety becomes concentrated upon this understandable cause. It is difficult for staff to deal with such a person. The patient may be terrified that her wound will burst, or that she will slip and fall again when attempting to walk on her broken leg. Similarly the habitual pessimism of the person with a depressive type of personality may hinder the active involvement required for full rehabilitation following serious illness. The marked swings of mood of a cyclothymic person may become very obvious when an individual requires long-term in-patient care.

Schizoid personality

Characteristically such people show withdrawal from social involvement and emotional coolness and detachment. It is not that they are shy or embarrassed when mixing, it is simply that they are aloof and do not require and are not interested in the company of other people. They are described by those who know them as loners; they are in fact solitary but not lonely, as they are quite self-sufficient.

Such people take their self-sufficient detachment into hospital or any other institution in which they are receiving care. They tend to be unpopular with other patients and staff, and efforts to 'jolly them along' or to encourage them to socialize meet with resistance. They are often stoical as far as their own sufferings are concerned and may appear callous with regard to the suffering of others.

Explosive personality

Such people give vent to totally unexpected outbursts of extremes of emotion. This may take the form of anger, amounting to violence, or extreme misery. They respond to emotional stimuli in the appropriate direction but often their rage seems to be out of all proportion to the severity of irritation to which they are exposed.

Obviously this sort of personality in a patient makes for difficulties for both staff and other patients. Other people tend to treat them extremely warily and they are likely to respond violently to the inevitable stresses, pressures and irritations that accumulate on a hospital ward during treatment.

Anankastic personality

This type of personality is commonly seen and is characterised by insecurity and extreme conscientiousness. Such people are rigid and perfectionist and are extremely sensitive about any criticism. They tend to be conformist in their manner of life, and like to obey orders to the letter and to carry out any task with the utmost thoroughness and attention to detail. They have difficulty making decisions because they only too readily see both sides of the question.

Such patients obey 'doctors' orders' implicitly; they co-operate in whatever treatment is prescribed for them and they do not default on taking medication or attending appointments. However, their perfectionism and sensitivity may make them tend to react very badly to being ill and consequently less than perfect in their ability to function. They are likely to show hypochondriacal symptoms and may become despondent about their capacity for improvement or adjustment.

Hysterical personality

Such people are histrionic, attention-seeking and theatrical; they are good at making superficial relationships and socializing but tend to have difficulty in sustaining long-term deep relationships.

Such people bring their theatricality into their relationships with doctors and nurses and their behaviour on the ward often seems to be a continual charade. They require the sociableness of the busy ward and need considerable encouragement and reassurrance. If they feel that they are not getting the attention they deserve, they may well provoke dramatic diversions. Once again it is important to recognise the existence of such a personality trait and to cope with the patient with both understanding and firmness.

Asthenic personality

Such people often appear inadequate, lacking in mental vigour, indecisive and weak-willed. They cope well when there is another strong person upon whom to rely but when this person, such as parent or spouse, is removed they may be unable to cope with life's difficulties and challenges. They readily establish dependent relationships.

The ease with which they assume dependence and submissiveness is the key to the ability of a person with asthenic personality disorder to be a model patient as long as they are in hospital care. However, re-establishing an independent life, returning to work and the responsibilities of managing a home, when they also have to cope with the residual disabilities after illness, may present insuperable problems to such people. They may follow the recovery from their physical illness with *illness behaviour* which appears to be aimed at remaining in long-term care and dependence.

Asocial personality

Such people are otherwise described as suffering from *psychopathic personality*. Characteristically they show callous lack of concern and an inability to learn from past mistakes. They are unable to feel the effect their unpleasant behaviour has upon other people, and although they show remorse when things go wrong they cannot really empathize with others. Although there is an association between this type of personality disorder and criminality, the overwhelming majority of criminals are not psychopathic and quite a large number of people with asocial personality do not have criminal records. This trait of personality is often associated with alcohol abuse and addiction to other drugs; they may arrive in the Accident and Emergency Department late at night with an unlikely story which is difficult to disprove. Males show this personality type more commonly than females. The temptation for hospital staff is to treat them with summary dismissal; however, their physical complaints are often genuine and require treatment just like any other patient.

These descriptions of personality should not be used in a rigid or immutable way. They encourage the doctor to observe his patient's consistent behaviour so that he can try to help the patient in the appropriate way. Normally people show a number of traits and characteristics, and it is useful to decide which of these traits are present to an abnormal degree; and then to ask oneself the question, does this abnormality of personality amount to personality disorder?

Further reading:

World Health Organization (1977) *International Classification of Diseases, Injuries and Causes of Death*, 9th Revision, Geneva, W.H.O.

CHAPTER 17

Stress and Coping

Doctors and lay people frequently describe someone as 'suffering from stress'. Although the general meaning of this statement seems to be clear, it raises some important questions. Is stress something external which happens to a person, for instance, or is it a process which happens within a person? Are some events inherently stressful, or is stress more a reflection of the individual's characteristics? These problems can be explored by considering three different, but all commonly used, definitions of stress; the stimulus-based definition, the response-based definition, and the interactional definition. The three definitions have all been useful in furthering our understanding of the nature of stress.

Three definitions of stress

Stimulus-based definition

This definition treats stress as a characteristic of the environment. The *Oxford Concise Medical Dictionary*, for instance, says: 'Stress is any factor that threatens the health of the body or has an adverse effect on its functioning, such as injury, disease or worry'.

This definition is particularly appealing when we consider major traumatic experiences, such as rape, hijacking, bereavement or imprisonment in a concentration camp, which most people would describe as extremely stressful. In these cases stress does seem to be a characteristic of the events which happen to people, and these events have been found to have a long-term impact on physical and psychological health. The research on *stressful life events* (Chapter

19) has shown how major events, or a string of minor events, may increase susceptibility to a wide range of disorders.

There are, however, two important limitations of this definition of stress. It assumes that undemanding situations are not stressful, whereas experience tells us that to human beings boredom and lack of stimulation can be stressful too. More importantly, it does not explain individual variation in response to situations assumed to be stressful. Particularly with minor events there is a great deal of variation in people's reactions, some appearing unaffected by the event and others reacting adversely to it. If stress is simply a property of the event, we would expect everyone's reaction to be similar, but this is clearly not the case.

Response-based definition

Stress can also be defined as a response, or pattern of responses, occurring within an individual. One of the most influential proponents of this view is Hans Selye, who wrote that: 'stress is the nonspecific physiological response of the body to any demand made upon it'. Selye considered that the stress response was essentially similar in many species, and by a 'nonspecific' response he meant that it did not vary when elicited by different sorts of stressor. The stress response was to be regarded as a universal pattern of defence reactions serving to protect the person or animal. He described three phases of this defence reaction, which he termed the *General Adaptation Syndrome* (GAS). First is an *alarm reaction*, in which physiological changes occur which prepare the individual to take some action, for instance to run away or to fight. If the threat does not overwhelm the individual, but still persists, the body continues to adapt to it. The second phase of longer-term adaptation he called *resistance*. The final phase of *exhaustion* occurs when the energy needed to adapt to the threat is used up. Selye's idea was that the physiological changes associated with the GAS were very effective in dealing with short-term threats, but that if the stage of resistance were prolonged, adverse effects would occur, leading to 'diseases of adaptation'. These would include all psychosomatic disorders, as well as allergies and other harmful immunological responses.

Although the response-based definition has been associated with valuable research, it also has the drawback that it portrays a person as the passive recipient or experiencer of stress. It cannot explain why different people react variously to the same event, nor does it suggest how stress may be prevented.

Interactional definition

According to the interactional definition, stress is best seen as a relationship between the person and his or her environment, a relationship in which people perceive an imbalance between the demand being made and the resources at their disposal. In other words, stress is not simply a feature of the environment or a bodily reaction, but describes the judgement or assessment that people have made of their situation and of their ability to cope with it. There are some situations, such as hijacking or bereavement, with which the majority of people would doubt their ability to cope, since the consequences threaten to be severe. Less serious events are experienced as stressful by fewer people, because more individuals feel able to cope with them. Examinations, for instance, are not equally threatening to everyone. The degree of threat here depends on such factors as the importance of the exam, how able or competent the person feels, and the amount of time they have to prepare for it.

This more sophisticated approach to the nature of stress is a useful one because it suggests that stress can be prevented by:
(1) removing the threat,
(2) improving people's coping resources, or
(3) altering the perception of the situation.
Psychological treatments of anxiety and depression rely mainly on strategies (2) and (3); while social methods of treatment are more likely to use (1). Because this approach emphasizes individual differences in the appraisal of stress, it needs to be complemented by an appreciation of those factors which, in general, help to predict when people are going to perceive a situation as demanding. Among the most demanding situations are those which involve *conflict* between two or more alternative actions. An *approach–avoidance* conflict is one in which the same action has both rewarding and punishing consequences, while an *approach–approach* conflict is one in which a person has to choose between two actions which are both likely to be rewarding. Conflict situations cease to be so demanding once the person is irrevocably committed to one

of the possible alternatives, or once the decision has effectively to be taken by someone else. On the whole people also find situations less demanding when they can *predict* or *control* what is to happen. When experiencing events like mild electric shocks, people prefer to know exactly when to expect the shock, and under these conditions the shocks also produce less physiological arousal. Finally, situations tend to be less demanding when there is adequate *social support*, that is when people can number among their resources other people who can advise and act as confidants.

Reactions to stress

Physiological

There are at least two major physiological reactions, both involving the adrenal glands, which occur in response to stressful situations such as hospital admission, flying or taking examinations. The *adrenal medulla* is regulated by a sympathetic nerve which stimulates the secretion of adrenaline and noradrenaline from the medulla. This *sympathetic-adrenomedullary* system appears to dominate during the alarm phase of the General Adaptation Syndrome. Adrenaline and noradrenaline, acting together with the sympathetic nervous system, rapidly mobilise the body's resources. Within minutes or even seconds there is an increase in heart rate and respiration rate, a release of stored red blood cells to convey more oxygen, a redirection of blood from the skin and viscera to the muscles and the brain, a rise in blood sugar, and other changes which enable the body to take immediate action.

Although present in the alarm phase, *adrenocortical activity* is thought to be particularly important during the second phase of resistance. The activity of the adrenal cortex is regulated mainly by the amount of adrenocorticotropic hormone (ACTH) in the blood, released by the anterior pituitary. The adrenal cortex produces several groups of steroid hormones, including cortisone. One of their effects is to raise the level of blood sugar, and it has been suggested that this is important to fuel the body's adaptation during the period of resistance. It should be noted, however, that these changes, if prolonged, have certain costs, such as a reduction in the body's ability to combat infection.

Psychological

Just as animals respond to danger by fight or flight, human beings may react to stressful situations by becoming aggressive or by escaping from or avoiding the situation. They may also prepare themselves in advance to cope with the situation more effectively. Lazarus has characterized these coping responses as involving *direct action* to change the environment, in contrast with other forms of coping in which people try to reduce their subjective feelings of distress. These *palliative* measures include symptom-directed ones such as the use of alcohol or tranquillisers, and intrapsychic measures such as denial, repression and intellectualization. These intrapsychic measures are also known as *defence mechanisms*, and represent a conscious or unconscious attempt on the part of the person to forget or somehow minimise the importance of their situation. Once again it should be noted that, although these coping responses may be effective in the short-term, over more prolonged periods they may themselves give rise to secondary problems which then exacerbate the person's situation.

Further reading:

Cox T. (1978) *Stress*, London, Macmillan.

CHAPTER 18

Behaviour Causing Illness

Most people do not seek to become ill, but suffer as a result of accidental exposure to infection, the proliferation of neoplastic cells, or some genetically determined metabolic dysfunction, to cite just three possibilities. Illness is generally a consequence of the 'slings and arrows of outrageous fortune'. However, a significant proportion of illness can be the direct result of the individual's own behaviour. The extent to which a particular person exposes him, or herself, to the possibility of the risk of illness varies considerably. In an individual case, any one of a number of factors might be relevant. Unconscious motivation is one, the person's perception of the risk is another, but probably the most important is the individual's assessment of the outcome of a piece of behaviour, in terms of the predicted reinforcement.

A decision is made, not necessarily consciously, as to the probable reward if the behaviour is shown, compared with the outcome if it is not. For example, do I play rugby and possibly gain the rewards of a sense of physical well-being, and the esteem of my peers if I score the winning try; together with the social rewards in the bar afterwards? Or, do I not play, thereby avoiding the possibility of being injured, but also missing out on the other rewards? Similarly, if I enjoy both horseriding and bellringing, but have a bad back; do I engage in these pleasurable activities and suffer physically afterwards, or do I avoid the physical discomfort but be miserable not doing the things I like? The *assessment of the payoff*, that is weighing up the various possible rewards and punishments against each other is one of the most fundamental processes at all levels of human behaviour, from the mundane 'do I have tea or coffee?', to the Shakespearean 'to be or not to be'. Where the outcomes are considered equal, the person will be in a state of conflict, usually of an approach–avoidance kind. As discussed in Chapter 17, conflict is often associated with illness in its own right.

Reasons for behaviour causing illness

We may distinguish two broad classes of illness-related behaviour. First, where the conflict, as discussed above is overt and the decision regarding action is a conscious one. For example, a person may know the risks of motor racing, but considers the rewards of the associated pleasurable experiences to outweigh them. The motivation is generally unexplored. Most people if asked why they do something, reply that they do it because they *like* it. The nature of the *liking* is generally obscure to the majority of persons. In fact, the reward may be explained in a number of ways: "I like motor racing because it:

(1) raises the level of my cortical arousal to its optimum,

(2) represents defiance of my safety-conscious father,

(3) boosts my esteem in the eyes of someone who is important to me,

(4) fulfills my self-image by identification with a childhood hero, or

(5) provides a socially acceptable route to suicide."

Clearly the number of possible explanations is infinite. The point is that the activity is engaged in because the predicted rewards are judged to be greater than the predicted negative outcomes.

The second, more important class of behaviours, is where the risks are again assessed at a cognitive level, and considered to outweigh the benefits of the behaviour. However, the person concerned is unable to change the behaviour even though they want to. In this instance, people do not behave rationally, the decision is influenced by emotional factors rather than intellectual ones. Since emotions are, by and large, outwith a person's control, the behaviour is also outwith this control. The processes relevant to the assessment of the predicted risk are considered in more detail in the context of health education in Chapter 29. This chapter is concerned with an elaboration of those factors thought to maintain illness-related behaviours.

The best known and undoubtedly the most medically important of these behaviours are cigarette smoking, drinking alcohol and eating foods high in carbohydrates and cholesterol. There is evidence that these activities, if engaged in to excess, significantly increase the risk that the individual concerned will develop a chronic illness and die earlier than otherwise. Smoking, drinking and eating are all voluntary behaviours in that we deliberately (that is, choose to) initiate them. But they do not seem to be voluntary (under our control) when we want to stop them, or to reduce their frequency. Even when our general practitioner, or some other prestigious figure, instructs us to lose weight say, we may find it difficult, despite apparent high motivation. One set of reasons for this is related to the communication process between doctor and patient. The doctor's instructions may be such that the patient does not comprehend or cannot remember them, or the instructions themselves may be inadequate. This is dealt with more fully in Chapter 25. However, a more powerful reason for patients being unable to change their behaviour is because the rewards are too great. If the *only* pleasure in your life comes from eating cream buns, you are unlikely to give it up simply because your doctor says it is bad for you.

One of the most potent factors in the maintenance of illness-related behaviours is the *time relationship* between the behaviour itself, the positive rewards, and the bad consequences (that is, the illness). As a general rule, for any sort of behaviour, the immediate consequences are the most powerful in determining the probability that it will be repeated. The immediate positive reward *now* of inhaling cigarette smoke, or tasting whisky are more significant to the individual than the unpleasantness of the bronchitis or the cirrhosis, in the future; or even the guilt at doing something your reason says is *harmful and thus wrong*. The precise nature of the immediate positive reward, of course, varies from one person to another, and is a function of their different learning histories. The nearness of the *discriminative stimuli* is also important in determining whether or not a particular behaviour is shown. Sitting at home with disapproving parents, it is easy not to smoke, and to resolve to stop smoking in the future. On the other hand, sitting in a friend's house, surrounded by the smell of smoke, and the sight of your friends smoking; if it is already an established habit, it is difficult to refrain.

The actual rewards associated with illness-related behaviour are many and varied, but may be classified into those associated with behaviours which lead to illness, and those associated with the consequences of illness. An example of the first type is the person who smokes for the physiological arousing effects of nicotine. The second type can be associated with any sort of illness; for example, the patient with a rare illness who feels *special* when paraded in front of students; the patient who gets more attention from her doctor than from her husband; the patient who is able to avoid unpleasant situations because of his illness. The *sick role* is discussed further in Chapter 20.

Accidents are a major source of illness, and if we accept that accidents do not *happen* but that they are made, then the behaviour associated with accidents can be thought of as illness-related. It is well-known that some people have more than their fair share of accidents, but the concept and determinants of the *accident-prone* personality are still somewhat vague. People who play a causative role in accidents may do so for a variety of reasons. The problem may be a cognitive one, involving the processes of attention and memory. It may be one of motor co-ordination, the person being excessively clumsy. There may be an emotional component, with the person's physiological arousal temporarily raised, so that their performance efficiency goes over the top of the inverted-U curve and begins to deteriorate. Accidents in this context are related to the person's ability or otherwise to recognise and to manage their response to stress. It is known, for example, that the more life changes a person experiences over a relatively short time period, the more likely they are to be involved in (by causing) a road traffic accident.

Once again, the material of this chapter has emphasised the importance of analysing a patient's presenting symptoms in a wider context. This allows, if adequately done, a more rational explanation of the illness to be developed, with the associated bonus of an elaboration of a rational treatment programme. Unravelling the sometimes complex motives behind the behaviour which is associated with an illness, can be rewarding for both the doctor and the patient. For the former because treatment should become more effective, and for the latter because their health should improve. The fundamental lesson to be learned is that human beings, by and large, are not entirely rational organisms.

CHAPTER 19

Social Causes of Disease

The notion that something about where, and in what style, we live has an influence upon our health has long historical roots in medicine. The study of the distribution and determinants of states of health in human populations is known as *epidemiology*. One of its earliest exponents, Hippocrates, noted in his book *Airs, Waters and Places*, associations between environmental factors and certain diseases. Snow's classic investigation of the 1855 cholera outbreak in London, which led to his identifying the source of the infection as the water from the Broad Street pump, is well-known. Similar investigations fuelled the public health movement in this country, which by cleansing water supplies and improving sanitation successfully defeated many lethal infectious disorders. Today rather more sophisticated methods are necessary because most of the outstanding medical problems appear to have a multiplicity of causes.

Causality

How are we able to say, with any degree of certainty, that one thing causes another to happen? To John Snow, the fact that cholera victims all shared the same source of water was sufficient for him to remove the pump handle, even though the discovery of the cholera bacillus by Koch had to wait a further 30 years. Today we talk easily about cigarette smoking *causing* cancer, but how does one set about establishing the relationship between the two? Armstrong (1980) has suggested that, simply put, three conditions must be met for causality to be inferred.

(1) *The correct time sequence.* It must be possible to demonstrate that one event precedes the other in time. This is not always easy to accomplish. For example, it has often been noted that higher rates of schizophrenia are recorded in inner-city areas. However, before concluding that poor housing conditions *cause* schizophrenia, it is first necessary to exclude the possibility that people already suf-

fering from the disorder do not move into areas of cheap housing. In fact, this latter, the so called *drift* hypothesis more closely fits the available evidence.

(2) *Statistical correlation.* There should be a degree of covariation between the two factors, and it should be possible to apply a statistical test to this variation in order to rule out the possibility that chance alone may have caused it. In our example, one would anticipate that the rates of schizophrenia would diminish as one moved out of the most poor areas of a city towards the more prosperous.

(3) *The absence of a confounding third variable.* A third variable, not considered in the original analysis, may account for the observed relationship between the two factors. For example, the correlation between living in a poor inner-city area and schizophrenia may be accounted for by the presence of a third factor, such as immigration. Immigrants, on first arrival, may be forced to live in inner-city areas out of economic necessity. The stress occasioned by adjusting to a new culture may make them more susceptible to schizophrenia, or alternatively the mental conflict occuring in early schizophrenia may have prompted them to emigrate.

Rarely, in investigations involving social factors, are simple linear models of causation found. More commonly, a multifactorial model involving both social and biological factors is necessary to explain the onset of disease.

Cultural differences

Diseases within a given population appear to follow regular patterns, which in part at least are attributable to underlying cultural patterns within a society. The process of industrialization sees a shift away from the infectious diseases as a major cause of death. These are replaced, as in our own society, by the degenerative diseases, cancer and cardiovascular disease. Other differences between cultural groups remain unexplained. Japan, for example, retains a low rate of heart disease in spite of industrialization. Incidence of stomach cancer, however, is higher in Japan than comparable industrialized societies. In an attempt to offer some explanations for this phenomenon, a study of 4000 Japanese–Americans domiciled in California showed that the Japanese who adhered to a more traditional lifestyle retained low rates of coronary heart disease.

In attempting to tease out the variables which may be at work it is sometimes difficult to separate cultural factors from geographical and even climatic ones. Explanations for the high rate of spina bifida in some parts of Ireland, for example, have included diet, lifestyle, and natural pollution.

Sub-cultural differences

Variations in the incidence of disease are not only detectable between nations, but also within them. Elsewhere (Chapter 22) we discuss the importance of social class in this respect. Different ethnic groups also display distinctive health patterns. Asians in Britain, for example, typically produce children of lower birth weight and have higher levels of perinatal and infant mortality than the indigenous population. Because of dietary differences, cases of anaemia, rickets and osteomalacia are also more common within this ethnic group. The use made of health services is also likely to vary between different sub-cultural groups, and indeed some minorities may have their own fully developed systems of alternative medicine.

Sex and marital status

Investigation of the effects of sex and marital status suggests that marriage can serve to protect people from, or make people more vulnerable to, illness. Women for instance are consistently found to be diagnosed more often as suffering from anxiety or depression; this may be due to a number of factors. The *feminine gender role* may be more congruent with the *sick role* than is the *masculine* role; that is it may be more socially acceptable for women to complain to their doctors about their feelings than it is for men. This interpretation is supported by the fact that women consult their general practitioners more often, and constitute the bulk of users of psychotropic drugs such as tranquillisers and antidepressants. If this was the whole story, it would be equally true for single and married women. However, data suggest that this pattern only holds for married women. Marriage increases the likelihood that women will be diagnosed as depressed, but decreases the likelihood that men will be.

A similar pattern holds true of mortality from diseases such as cirrhosis of the liver, lung cancer, tuberculosis and diabetes, and also of death by homicide and suicide. For men marriage appears to act as a protective factor, while for women it either offers less protection or increases their vulnerability. This has led to the idea that men receive more benefits from marriage than women, whose role in a traditional marriage may produce less satisfaction and make more demands on her. Contrary to the popular belief that unmarried women are frustrated and unhappy, there is evidence that, as far as health is concerned, they may be better off. Preliminary data from the U.S.A. indicate that changes in male and female gender roles, largely brought about by the women's movement, seem to have had the effect of reducing the discrepancy between male and female rates of depression.

Life events

The idea that stressful events in our everyday lives may result in illness is commonplace. Our everyday speech is rich in expressions such as 'this is driving me mad', or 'this job will be the death of me'. Following Freud's psychoanalytic investigations there developed the concept of *psychosomatic disorders*. Diseases such as asthma, peptic ulcerisation and eczema were believed to be caused or exacerbated by unresolved and largely unconscious psychological tensions. This is now considered to be an over-simplification.

Similarly, it has long been understood that a major event, such as bereavement, brings with it an increased risk of physical and psychiatric illness. It has been demonstrated that widows are more vulnerable to premature death, especially from heart attacks, during the first 6 months following their bereavement. Again common speech, with expressions like 'dying of a broken heart' has long recognised this phenomenon.

In more recent years *life event* research has widened in order to consider the possible impact that a variety of life changes may have upon our vulnerability to a broad range of diseases. A social readjustment rating scale has been developed which allows a numerical weighting to be assigned to a number of events such as marriage, divorce, moving house, etc. By summing these weights a cumulative life events score may be arrived at, although it appears just as effective to make a simple count of the number of events experienced.

In a prospective study, life events were recorded initially and health records obtained after a lapse of some nine months. On the basis of the scores respondents were placed in one of three groups, high, medium and low-risk. Subsequent illness was reported in 49%, 25% and 9% of persons respectively in these groups.

The relationship between life events and illness is a complex one, and in Chapter 17 we considered what makes some events 'stressful'. In many instances the presence of life events may not be causal, but may act as a trigger mechanism in the presence of other factors, or exacerbate a condition that under other circumstances might have been tolerated. This is an active area of research, and the number of conditions now implicated by life event work grows wider all the time. The following are some of the conditions now thought to be affected by the occurrence of life events: acne, asthma, amenorrhea, arthritis, cancer, common cold, coronary heart disease, diabetes, depression, duodenal ulcer, epilepsy, glaucoma, hypertension, insomnia, low back pain, leukaemia, migraine, neurodermatitis, stroke, pre-menstrual tension, post-operative infection, tension headache, ulcerative colitis.

Investigations of the relationship between life events and de-pressive illness in women, have demonstrated a raised incidence of depression among a sample of working-class London women relative both to middle-class women and women living on an Hebridean island. Four 'vulnerability factors' have been identified: absence of intimate relationship with a male; no employment out-side the home; loss of mother before the age of 11 years; and the presence of three or more children under the age of 15 years living at home. A woman experiencing a severe life event, in the presence of these vulnerability factors, was found to be at a high risk for depressive illness.

Conclusions

There is now considerable evidence that social factors may be part of the causal chain leading to disease, both in major causes of death such as cardiovascular disease and cancer, and in other disorders which account for the greatest proportion of lost working days such as respiratory diseases, mental disorders, accidents, and musculoskeletal diseases like rheumatoid arthritis. Understanding the complicated causal chains in these cases may enable us to inter-vene more effectively. It is unlikely that any cure for lung cancer would be as effective as prohibiting the sale of cigarettes.

The imbalance of diseases between social classes, particularly those affecting young children, would suggest that we should shift resources towards community care, with more health monitoring in schools, greater emphasis upon preventive measures, and a more equitable distribution of resources, favouring those inner-city areas which are currently poorly served. The greatest improvements in health care would be made by attending to factors earlier in the chain of causation. By simply responding to the manifestations of disease, clinical medicine resembles a fire-brigade, constantly rushing to the site of a new blaze, and rarely pausing to examine the cause of the fire nor considering the need for sprinkler systems and extinguishers.

Further reading:

Armstrong D. (1980) *An Outline of Sociology as Applied to Medicine.* Bristol, Wright.

Tuckett D., ed. (1976) *An Introduction to Medical Sociology.* London, Tavistock.

CHAPTER 20

Social Basis of Illness and Illness Behaviour

The study of health and illness is not only a study of biological processes within a patient's body, but involves also the actions that patients take to maintain or to restore their health. The actions that occur in response to a person's suspicion or perception of being ill are usually known as *illness behaviour*, a term designed to draw attention to the many different ways in which someone might respond to feeling ill. Social scientists have pointed out that these responses are shaped by the attitudes to, and understanding of, illness possessed by the social groups of which the person is a part, and cannot be predicted solely from a knowledge of the diseases from which they are suffering. From the patients' perspective, then, social factors influence the likelihood that they will consult and subsequently comply with treatment. But from the doctor's perspective too, social factors can be seen to influence what is regarded as a disease and what is regarded as normal.

The patient's perspective: Why go to a doctor?

The traditional biological view of consultation is a straightforward one: a person contracts a disease, begins to feel ill, and so consults a doctor for treatment. If this were an adequate account, we would expect:

(1) that most people who feel ill consult their doctor,

(2) that people with serious demonstrable pathology receive treatment, and

(3) that people who do consult their doctor usually reveal some significant pathology.

Results from numerous community surveys, however, contradict these assumptions. Often well over half the people interviewed have had at least one painful or distressing symptom in the previous fortnight, but less than one-third of these have consulted. In other studies 20% or upward of randomly selected people have been found to be in need of investigation and possibly treatment. The proportion of serious undiagnosed disease is even higher among the elderly, where disease can be difficult to distinguish from the effects of ageing. On the other hand, some general practitioners often complain that at least half their consultations are trivial and inappropriate. So, contrary to the simple biological model, only a minority of people who feel ill actually consult their doctors, there are many people with serious undiagnosed pathology, and many consultations reveal no substantial pathology. The study of illness behaviour helps to explain why this is so.

Why people do not go to the doctor

If people are to consult their doctors, they must recognize that their symptoms are abnormal, they must decide that consultation is appropriate and they must not be dissuaded by the costs of consultation.

Recognising symptoms as abnormal

We have already noted that recognizing abnormality may be more difficult for elderly people. Symptoms such as tiredness, headache and low back pain may be so common that they are ignored by many people. People tend to think their health is better than do the doctors who examine them, and this is particularly true of dental health. In part this is due to lack of medical knowledge, but may also be due to the prevailing culture which accepts certain symptoms as normal because of their ubiquity. These factors will contribute to the under-reporting of illness.

Selecting the appropriate response

Even if people recognise their symptoms to be abnormal, there are a variety of actions they may take depending on their understanding of the causes and cure of illness. Some religious sects, for instance, may forbid the use of medical procedures in favour of spiritual cures. The use of prayer or penance makes sense if the cause of the symptoms is perceived as supernatural, as a punishment for sinful behaviour perhaps, or for failing to observe proper rites. It has been observed that cancer patients may sometimes see their disease as a punishment, and prefer to indulge feelings of guilt by taking no action over their symptoms. Many alternative practitioners, such as homeopaths, chiropractors, faith healers, acupuncturists and osteopaths, may also be seen as more appropriate for certain medical conditions, particularly those chronic ones where scientific medicine has been least successful. Finally, the most common method of treating symptoms appears to be self-medication, with patent medicines easily outnumbering prescribed medicines.

The costs of consultation

The financial costs of consultation are more evident in private health care systems, but even within a free National Health Service there may be hidden penalties. Losing time from work to attend surgery is more likely to mean a loss of earnings for manual than for clerical workers. Increases in charges for prescriptions, for glasses, and for dental care are likely to reduce consultation among the low-paid. Then there are psychological costs. Admitting illness is upsetting to many people who may have been brought up to see it as a form of weakness, as something not to give in to. Some people may avoid consulting because they are afraid of discovering some serious pathology or are afraid of investigations or hospital treatment. Their anxiety about the symptoms may be easier to put up with. Finally, there are the social costs of entering the *sick role* and the obligations which this entails. As a patient one is expected to submit to medical procedures which are sometimes unpleasant, painful or embarrassing. Many people are unhappy about relinquishing their usual duties and becoming temporarily dependent on others, while old people may be anxious that they may no longer be allowed to look after themselves. All these costs may appear insignificant to doctors and yet they play a major part in determining whether or not a person chooses to consult.

Why people do go to the doctor

Consultation is likely to occur if it is seen as an appropriate reaction to recognized symptoms, and if the benefits are likely to outweigh the costs. It has also been suggested that consultation is often prompted by a *trigger* which is social rather than biological in nature.

The benefits of consultation

Among the psychological benefits is the reduction of anxiety about the meaning of the symptoms and about their implications. Symptoms are often strange and worrying to people, and reassurance is more effective when it comes from a person perceived as high in status or expertise. There is also evidence that those low in social support, without friends or confidants, consult more. Some patients may be primarily in need of a confiding relationship which is not otherwise available. The social benefits which accrue from the sick role have already been mentioned. Patients are traditionally released from many of the obligations of everyday life, such as going to work and looking after other family members. Since patients are not usually regarded as being responsible for their illness, they may enjoy greater latitude in their behaviour. A period of illness may thus relieve people temporarily from some of the burden of their normal responsibilities.

Social triggers

In many cases people seem to adapt to their symptoms. Rather than seek aid at their physically sickest point, they wait until prompted by some other event. This might be a family or personal crisis, from which they can use their symptoms as a justification for escaping. Alternatively, they may wait until the symptoms interfere with their lives in some important way, such as stopping them working or meeting others. They may wait until someone else tells them to see a doctor, or until the symptoms have lasted for a specific length of time. These triggers are independent of, but operate in conjunction with, the presence of symptoms to determine when consultation occurs. Different ethnic groups, such as Irish and Italian Americans, have been found to employ different sorts of trigger.

The doctor's perspective: the nature of disease

Most medical concepts of disease involve the idea of abnormality or pathology contrasted with normality or health. But it is not possible to distinguish the healthy from the pathological purely in terms of statistical frequency. For one thing, many disorders are not either present or absent but represent, as in the case of hypertension or diabetes mellitus, one end of a continuous distribution. Statistics cannot decide at which precise point the condition becomes pathological. Then there are conditions, such as atherosclerosis or dental caries, which although seen as pathological are statistically normal in certain populations. The idea of disease additionally implies a socially undesirable condition, one which has adverse social consequences. It is hard to see, for instance, how dyslexia, a type of reading difficulty, could exist in a pre-literate culture where failure to read conveyed no social disadvantage. Similarly, in one South American tribe, it is the *absence* of a facially disfiguring skin condition which is defined as a disease, because this singles out an individual and puts him or her at a social disadvantage. This social aspect of disease helps to explain why dissidents in the U.S.S.R. may be diagnosed as schizophrenic. In the past some doctors regarded homosexuality as an illness because they conceived it as conveying a disadvantage, not primarily to the person, but to society.

The conclusion of this chapter is that health and illness need to be regarded, whether from the patient's or from the doctor's perspective, as both social and biological phenomena.

Further reading:

Tuckett D., ed. (1976) *An Introduction to Medical Sociology.* London, Tavistock. (See especially Chapters 5 and 10.)

CHAPTER 21

Old Age and its Problems

There has been a profound shift in the balance of our society since the turn of the century. The proportion of people who are economically dependent, school children and the elderly, has remained at 40%, but in that time the elderly (65 +) have increased from 6% of the population to the present 17%.

By the end of this century the proportion will remain the same (17%), but we will experience a growth in the number of *old elderly*: those over 75 will increase by 20%, whilst the number of people over 85 are expected to double in that time. This group of old elderly will pose particular problems since the demand for medical and social services is known to climb rapidly in those over 75. Because women outlive men, about two-thirds of this group will be female, many living alone.

Older people are not evenly distributed throughout the population, and this may cause particular difficulties for service planners. Some inner-city areas contain high proportions of elderly, many living in some of our most deteriorated housing. Retirement migration, particularly to certain seaside resorts, may result in as many as 40% of the population in these towns being over retirement age.

Substantial sums of public money are involved in maintaining older people; for example, retirement and supplementary pensions now account for 17% of all public expenditure and over 5% of the country's gross national product. In addition it has been estimated that, as a group, the elderly absorb more than one-third of all expenditure on social programmes such as:

special housing,

health care in hospital and at home,

social and domiciliary services, and
travel and fuel subsidies.

Health

Health is a major concern for older people since it is related to their ability to retain independence. In spite of this, studies have found many cases of unreported illness. This is probably due to the low expectations of health that many older people have: 'you can't expect anything else at my age' being a typical attitude. This is a view which seems to permeate some of the helping professions, and may lead to an over-pessimistic view of the patient, and consequent therapeutic inactivity.

National surveys of those elderly who live at home produce the following picture:

50% report some disability,

35% report some disability which limits activity,

13% are physically handicapped in that 'Living activities are severely restricted',

4% of those living at home are bedfast or housebound,

20% of those living at home who are over 85 are permanently bedfast.

In the average general practice about 20% of all consultations are with the over 65s. The demands made increase with age, and for any given 2-week period it may be anticipated that 14% of G.P. consultations are from those aged 65–74, while the over 75s make up about 17% of consultations.

Moreover, it has been estimated that over 22% of the elderly, within a typical practice, are suffering from some form of psychiatric morbidity (most frequently depression), much of it undiagnosed.

Community health services

The *general practitioner*, as we have already indicated, has an important part to play in the health care of the elderly. Two-thirds of his consultations with the over 75s take place at home. However, in recent years, the use of paramedical staff in this field has increased. *District nurses*, many attached to general practices, have expanded in number and role; offering a night nursing service, for example.

Health visitors, too, have increased their visiting to the elderly. Both are becoming more involved with health-screening, health education, and preventative programmes.

Hospital-based *occupational therapists* play a vital role in rehabilitation, and may follow the discharged patient into their home, offering advice and instruction with daily tasks, such as cooking. Their specialist knowledge is also important in arranging for appropriate aids and adaptations to the home.

Chiropody services are important in maintaining mobility. Many community surveys have demonstrated how feet problems, even the inability to cut toenails (20%), may have wide ranging social repercussions. An inability to visit friends, or go on shopping trips, reduces the size of the older person's social world.

The *opthalmic, pharmaceutical*, and *dental* services also all contribute to the general wellbeing of older people.

Care in the community

Great emphasis has been placed, in recent years, upon enabling people who may be frail or disabled to remain in their own homes. Surveys indicate that 65% of the physically disabled are aged over 65. Various forms of financial support are available to such people including, a mobility allowance for those unable to walk, attendance allowances for those who need continual supervision, and invalidity pensions. Local *social services departments* also provide a range of services for the elderly:

social work support,
meals on wheels,
home helps,
aids and adaptations to the home,
day centres,
luncheon clubs, and
emergency alarm call systems.

Voluntary organizations, sometimes in conjunction with social services, may also offer help such as transportation, assistance with shopping, home visiting and other services.

In spite of claims that the provision of such services undermines the role of the family, most of the evidence indicates that younger family members maintain regular contact with their elders, and provide a good deal of support. The size of the pool of available helpers, however, may be affected by recent social changes, for example smaller families, fewer unmarried women, more married women working and greater mobility.

Services in the future may well be geared towards helping families to care for their elderly relatives. Such schemes as holiday relief, rotating hospital and residential care, incontinence laundry services and relatives support groups are all examples of moves in this direction.

Institutional care

With the modern emphasis upon community care, many authorities had anticipated a run down in residential provision. However, the increasing number of the very old has prevented this happening. The development of *sheltered housing*, now catering for 5% of the elderly and offering specially designed accommodation, with an alarm system and resident warden, has contributed towards community care.

Any form of *institutional care* is faced with the dilemma of how to offer support without undermining independence and autonomy. It has been argued that in this regard we have failed, thus: '..... (the residents) are subtly orientated towards a system in which they submit to orderly routine, lack creative occupation and cannot exercise much self-determination' (Townsend)

At any one time about 5% of the elderly are in some form of institutional care. In the health service half the total beds and 40% of the acute beds are occupied by elderly people, whilst within psychiatric hospitals old people constitute the largest group. Those aged over 75 currently occupy one-third of all hospital beds, so that the impact of their increasing numbers over the next twenty years on the hospital service is plain. Increasingly the emphasis, within hospitals, is being placed upon rehabilitation, and, wherever possible, a return home.

Residential homes (*Part III homes*) are also available for those unable to continue living at home, but not thought to require hospital care. Local authorities provide the bulk of the 150 000 or so places available, although private and voluntary organisations also contribute. It has been claimed that between 20–40% of these residents could remain in the community with home improvements and more domiciliary support, but since the average age of admission is 82 and still rising, this is becoming less likely.

There has been a view that what some elderly people require is a nursing home environment. This would offer a better quality of life than is possible on the rather clinical and impersonal hospital ward, and yet provide the appropriate medical and nursing services. Experimental schemes are being developed on this model, and, when evaluated, may provide a wider range of provision than is currently available.

Retirement and adjustment in later life

Growing older is not simply a biological phenomenon. It involves a complex series of social and psychological processes. For many the point at which one enters *old age* is *retirement*. Increasingly, as more women are drawn into full-time employment, this is becoming a major life event for both sexes. Retirement signifies not simply giving up a job but also the loss of many significant roles. People tend to be identified in our society by the work they do, he *is* a policeman or she *is* a doctor. Retirement undermines part of our identity as well as cutting us off from former colleagues and friends. As a consequence of retirement most people face living on a lower income, some even poverty. The day will have lost much of its routine and organisation, and, perhaps for the first time, the individual is faced with considerable amounts of free time. Not going out to work also means considerably more time spent at home, and this may cause problems of adjustment between husband and wife.

Every year about half a million people retire in Britain. Some may have prepared for this change, even gone through a transitional period, when their working hours were reduced. But only 6% of those who retire receive any formal preparation. Information and advice about such matters as leisure pursuits, health maintenance, nutrition, educational opportunities, and financial planning may help to make this period of life a positive experience. Employers, trades unions, local education departments, and various voluntary bodies are trying to develop such programmes.

Old age, as we have noted already, results for some people in reduced physical activity. But all face bereavement and loss as close relatives and friends begin to die. This poses problems not only of adjusting to that loss, but also of coming to terms with one's own impending death. It has been suggested that old age in Western societies is typified by a slow and mutually satisfying withdrawal of the older person from the surrounding world (*disengagement*).

Debate has centred upon the issue of how far such a withdrawal is imposed upon older people, for example by lack of resources.

It seems more likely that each person ages in his or her own individual way, and that this reflects in large measure their earlier *biography* or *career*. This is important since any cohort should not be seen simply as *old people* but also as people who were, say, young in 1910. Their present attitudes and behaviour cannot simply be attributed to being old, but must also be accounted for in terms of their earlier socialization and life experiences.

Similarly, general theories about the psychology of ageing have come under challenge. Many of our stereotypes about older people's slowness and inability to learn have not found support when put to the test. Any slowing down appears to be made good by experience and, if motivated, older people may learn as readily, if in slightly different ways, as younger people.

The future

More older people are surviving to live out a healthier, more active, old age. Often we have too gloomy a picture because most of the evidence that we have about this period of life is obtained from those experiencing difficulties. We also approach older people with a stereotyped view which too often robs them of their individuality and casts them as 'a problem'. The challenge of an ageing population is not met by simply providing more of the services we have described, as these often rely upon a *crisis model*, which only intervenes when things go wrong. What we must do, in concert with older people, is develop new ways in which, by prevention and self-care, many of these crises may be avoided or contained.

Further reading:

Carver V. & Liddiard P., ed. (1978) *An Ageing Population*, London, Hodder and Stoughton in Association with The Open University Press.
Townsend P. (1962) *The Last Refuge*. London, Routledge and Kegan Paul.

CHAPTER 22

Work, Social Class and Health

In Britain, until the recent rapid increase in unemployment, about half the population spent almost half their waking hours outside their homes in some form of paid work. Since World War II increasing numbers of married women have chosen to continue in employment, so that by 1977 over half of them (68% for the 35–54 year olds) were working.

The actual work environment may have a considerable influence upon a person's health. But so also may the particular set of attitudes, beliefs and lifestyle associated with people who work in a particular industry, or share an occupational grouping. The categorization of people by the type of job they do is usually referred to as *social* or *occupational class*.

The work environment

The nature of the work we do varies widely; as do the pressures that it places us under, and the health risks to which it exposes us. Some people do jobs which others consider to be play, such as professional sportsmen and singers, whilst other people indulge in leisure activities which demand a vast expenditure of energy, and involve them in risk, for instance climbers and potholers.

Some jobs are by their very nature more dangerous than others either because they take place in high risk situations, such as fishing and coalmining, or because the industrial processes involved create a noxious environment, for example fumes, dust, or extreme heat. Injury to health or death may come suddenly as in an electric shock or a roof fall, or more insidiously as with asbestosis, bronchitis or certain specific forms of cancer. So well known are some of the associations between work and health that the disorders engendered have taken the name of the occupation: potter's rot and painter's colic, for example; whilst the expression, 'as mad as a hatter' derives from the fact that workers in the felt hat industry faced a high risk of mercury poisoning.

Work and stress

The concept of stress was used by Hans Selye to classify a number of disorders invoked experimentally in animals which were believed to be related to the hyperfunction of the adrenal cortex (see Chapter 17). Subsequent writers have developed and extended his notion and tried to apply it to a number of human disorders.

It is commonplace nowadays for a person's work to be described as *stressful*, and for certain disorders, such as stomach ulcers, to be attributed to this. However, the literature which examines work as a source of stress is extremely complex and as one reviewer has commented, 'theory outruns the data'. It is one thing to demonstrate, sometimes under laboratory conditions, that bodily changes take place as the result of work pressures, but quite another to relate these to longer term effects which result in illness.

Particular patterns of work have been shown to increase stress reactions within the body. In one study the effects of moving from hourly rates of pay in a sweet factory to piece work (payment for what you produce) were examined. The changeover resulted in a measurable increase in catecholamines, which is commonly associated with stress reactions.

A similar type of study noted that the blood pressure of air-traffic controllers rose quite remarkably when they went on duty. Work stresses, of these kinds, are usually associated in the general public's mind with various forms of cardiovascular disorder. However, little convincing evidence about the long-term effect of work stress has so far emerged. For example, a study in the U.S.A. sought to relate the number of job changes (transfers, promotions) to the onset of heart disease. The study did not support the widely held view that those who gained most promotion, or took on apparently more demanding jobs, had higher rates of heart disease than others in the company. In fact none of the measures relating to changes and transfers correlated significantly with the incidence of heart disease.

Friedman and Rosenman have attempted to relate coronary heart disease to two behavioural patterns. Type 'A' people are described as aggressive, competitive, always under pressure, and racing against the clock (characteristic of the go-getting executive). Type 'B' personalities are more relaxed and less impatient. They were found by Friedman and Rosenman to have only half the risk of heart disease compared to the type 'A' group.

It is unlikely, however, that any simple relationship exists between the demands of work, personality and heart disease. The coping mechanisms of the individual are likely to be just one of many intervening variables. Evidence from epidemiological surveys indicate that rates of coronary heart disease are in fact higher in the lower social class groups (IV and V) than they are in the higher ones (I and II), but one might suppose that more of the ambitious, driving Type 'A' personalities, would be found in the higher social groups. A recent study of British civil servants produced further evidence demonstrating that the higher grade civil servants had the lower rates of heart disease.

Job loss

The evidence about the impact of job loss is also not clear cut. Some people have suggested that retirement is a major cause of stress-induced illness. However, there is little evidence to support this view, and just as important would seem to be the concurrent substantial drop in income which follows retirement.

Similarly a number of authors have sought to relate levels of illness to unemployment and redundancy. Much of the work has been upon small cohorts and remains unconvincing. Kasl and Cobb examined the health levels of American workers at two factories, just before, and then following a closure. They recorded an increased rate of ill-health before the anticipated closure and raised levels of self-reported stress. However, following the factories' closure the evidence of increased illness was less pronounced, although raised blood pressure and serum cholestrol levels were discovered.

With unemployment an increasing problem in our society it seems the investigation of links between job loss and ill-health is becoming more important.

Working conditions

Actual working conditions vary very widely between occupational groups. We noted earlier how some jobs expose the workers to greater risks than others, but they also vary in the hours required and the pattern of life demanded.

About one-quarter of all manual workers are on some form of shift system. These vary in the pattern of hours demanded, but may create problems associated with disturbance of sleeping, eating and socialization. Less than 5% of professionals and managers have to work to a shift system. Manual workers also tend to be given less holiday than their white-collar counterparts: 3–4 weeks as compared with 5–6 weeks.

Manual work is likely to be routinized and require little initiative. This may result in boredom, a factor which correlates with industrial injuries. They are also more tightly supervised and subject to stricter discipline than white-collar workers. The majority have to clock-in when they start work, and lose money if they miss any time, unlike professionals who are simply paid a salary. This has important implications for health care, since a visit to a doctor or a clinic may result in broken time and loss of income for some people, but not others. Manual workers may be dismissed at short notice, few having conditions of service which compare with those offered to people in the professional ranks. Similarly their job is more likely to be undermined by seasonal variations and swings in the economic cycle which also affect level of earnings.

The concept of social class

Most societies are hierarchical in structure, that is some people either because of age, wisdom, wealth or power are seen as more important than others. You might like to examine the environment in which you work and note the different strata which exist and the hierarchical form it takes. A person's position in the hierarchy is likely to determine what rights, privileges and duties they have, as well as affecting the way they view themselves and their relationships with others.

In an industrial society the individual's place within the hierarchy is related to the type of work they do. Thus a simple definition of *social class* is '... a grouping of people into categories on the basis of occupation'.

In Britain we have relied upon ascertaining social class by reference to the husband's occupation. In other countries, like the U.S.A., multidimensional scales tend to be used, which incorporate such factors as income and education. Occupational grading has however proved simple to use, and remains a powerful way to highlight inequalities between groups of people.

Determination of social class

The classificatory system, used since 1911, divides occupation into five categories. One of the categories is conventionally subdivided into two. Males are allocated a grading on the basis of their occupation, details of which are contained in the Registrar General's classification of occupations. Married women and children are classified according to the husband's/father's occupation. Those who are retired or unemployed are dealt with by referring back to their last significant job, whilst single women are classified according to their own occupation.

The present distribution of social class is detailed in the Table 22.1.

TABLE 22.1. The Registrar General's classification of social class

Social Class		Examples	Population %	Generic Group
I	Established professions, senior administrative, owners of large businesses	Doctors, company directors	5	Middle class or White collar
II	Administrative, managerial, lesser professions	Civil servants, school teachers, social workers	20	
III N.M.	Skilled non-manual	Clerical workers	15	
III M.	Skilled manual	Joiners, electricians	33	Working class or Blue collar
IV	Semi-skilled manual	Machine operatives, farm workers	19	
V	Unskilled manual	Labourers	8	

The concept of social class has proved to be a powerful analytical tool in epidemiological studies, which have demonstrated that death and disease is not randomly distributed throughout the population. Inequalities in income, social status and opportunities are reflected in inequalities in health. However, as noted in Chapter

19, the question of causality is difficult to answer, especially when a concept as broad as social class is being invoked.

Social class and birth

The Black Committee, which reported in 1980 upon the state of the nation's health, noted that class differences in mortality are a constant feature of the human lifespan. Their report paid particular attention to the disparities to be found between different classes during the first year of life. For example 8.2% of babies born to parents of social class IV or V had a birth weight of less than 2.5 g, compared with 4.5% from classes I and II. In Scotland the neonatal and postneonatal death rate per 1000 is 9 for social class I, but 18 for class V.

Social class and death

Death before retirement is two-and-a-half times more likely among class V males, and their wives, than it is among the professional group (class I). If age-standardized death rates, between the ages of 15–64 years are examined, then the rate for class V men is a little under twice (1.8) that of class I men.

Access to and use of health services

Ease of access to health facilities has an impact upon their usage. It has been suggested that in Britain an *inverse care law* applies, in that the provision of health care (number, quality of doctors and other factors) is inversely related to those areas and people most in need (North of England, industrial cities). To take just one example, it has been found that the need for and provision of child health services is negatively correlated with a number of indicators of need such as levels of infant mortality, stillbirth rates and numbers of teenage and unmarried mothers.

The *costs* of visiting a surgery, both financial and in terms of time are greater for those who have to lose time from work, income and have to make use of public transport, all factors associated with working-class groups. Physical proximity to a surgery also affects the likelihood of attendance particularly for the elderly and disabled.

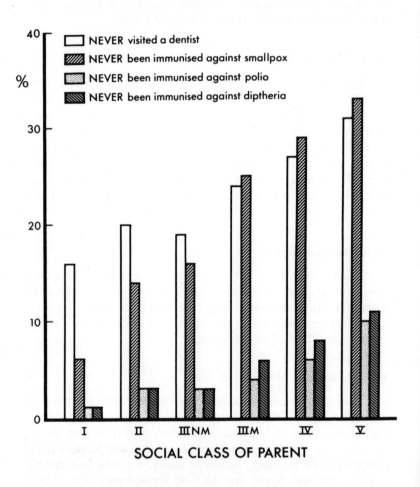

FIG. 22.1. Use of preventive services by children aged under 7 years.

The use of *preventive services* is also related to social class. This is demonstrated in Fig. 22.1. A number of reasons may be advanced to explain this. The cost and accessibility element already referred to may be one, others may include lack of knowledge, and greater feelings of passivity and helplessness in those from social classes IV and V.

Conclusion

Henry Sigerist, writing in 1943, noted that: 'Poverty remains the chief cause of disease, and it is a factor which is beyond the immediate control of medicine'.

The Black Report, which examined the state of health in Britain more than 30 years after the National Health Service was established noted that while there has been some general improvement in health the inequalities between social classes were in some cases widening: 'Present social inequalities in health in a country with substantial resources like Britain are unacceptable, and deserve so to be declared by every section of public opinion'.

What this means in concrete terms is spelt out clearly in this further comment: 'Average life expectancy provides a useful summary of the cumulative impact of these advantages and disadvantages throughout life. A child born to professional parents, if he or she is not socially mobile, can expect to spend over 5 years more living'.

Further reading:

Black Report (1980) *Inequalities in Health*, London, D.H.S.S.
Townsend P. & Davidson, N., Eds (1982) *Inequalities in Health*. London, Penguin.

CHAPTER 23

Doctor–Patient Communication

In listening to doctors and patients one hears frequent reports of *communication difficulties*. By this people seem to mean one of two things: either some unavoidable interference from an external factor, like a bad telephone connection, or an unwillingness on the part of the other person to *listen* to what was being said. In both cases the implication is that such difficulties are inevitable. Rather than accept this point of view, it may be more constructive to ask how common and how serious such difficulties are, how they can best be explained, and what can best be done about them.

Evidence for communication difficulties

Relevant evidence comes from two main sources: from the patient's point of view, how satisfied they are with medical communication; and from the doctor's point of view, how successfully the patients remember advice and carry out instructions.

Patient satisfaction

Although most patients express overall satisfaction with the medical care they receive, the one notable exception is their satisfaction with communications. Between 10 and 60% of discharged patients report being dissatisfied and having wanted more information. Complaints about the lack of information have generally been upheld when investigators have attended consultations or have studied verbal transcripts of them. Further insight into patient satisfaction is provided by a study of 800 consultations at a walk-in children's clinic in America. On average only 5% of the doctors' conversation was personal or friendly, and yet the amount of non-medical or sociable conversation was directly related to the mothers' satisfaction with the visit. The more satisfied the mothers were, the more likely they were to carry out the prescribed treatment. It is interesting to note that most of the doctors thought they had been friendly, but less than half the patients shared this impression. In this study, satisfaction was also related to another of the patients' major goals: feeling that their main concerns had been dealt with. On average, only a quarter of their concerns and worries were actually discussed at the consultation.

Remembering and following advice

In the study at the children's clinic it was found that when interviewed after the consultation nearly half the women were unclear about what had caused their child's illness. Moreover, less than half of them had carried out the doctor's advice in full. These discouraging findings are not at all atypical, however. On average about 45% of medical information gets forgotten almost immediately, while roughly one-half of all patients can be expected not to follow the advice they have been given.

Explaining communication failures

Three main types of explanation have been proposed for dissatisfaction with doctor–patient communication, focussing respectively on patient characteristics, cognitive processes and motivational processes.

Patient characteristics

Doctors sometimes suggest that certain patients complain or are unco-operative, no matter what efforts are made on their behalf. In other words this behaviour is directly attributable to their personality. Although this may be true in individual cases, no consistent personality differences have been found that distinguish dissatisfied or noncompliant patients. Similarly, they do not differ systematically by age, sex, race, marital status, social class or intelligence. This is not to say that these variables are *always* irrelevant, but they do not help a *general* understanding of the problem. Moreover, many patients appear to be dissatisfied just with communications while remaining perfectly satisfied with other aspects of medical care, which again suggests that explanations of communication difficulties should be sought elsewhere.

Cognitive processes

Communication problems may also occur because patients do not understand or do not remember what they are told. *Failures of understanding* may be due to lack of medical knowledge or to the complexity of the information presented. It has been shown that many people do not know the location of most of the organs of the body, and may have quite misleading theories about how the body works. This lack of knowledge might cause them to place a different interpretation on what they are told from that which the doctor intended. Many doctors also use medical terms with which patients are not familiar, and provide information in too complex a form. The complexity of written material can be calculated using a formula based on the number of syllables in the words used and on the length of the sentences. By this means many leaflets produced by doctors can be shown to be too difficult for as much as half the population to read. Some studies show that errors in taking medication may be greatly reduced by providing leaflets which have been rewritten so that they are easy to understand.

We have already seen that *failures of memory* are extremely common. As might be expected, the more information that is provided the more is forgotten. There is some evidence that mentioning material early in a consultation leads to better recall. This is potentially important, since advice and instructions are usually among the last items mentioned, but are the most significant for the patient. Putting certain items first in the consultation may lead to better recall of those items, but the total amount recalled will remain much the same.

Four alternative methods have been suggested for increasing the total amount of information recalled:

(1) The first method is to increase the *comprehensibility* of written material by using shorter words and sentences.

(2) The second method, known as *explicit categorisation*, consists of the doctor categorising the material for the patient and announcing and repeating the category names. For instance: 'I am going to tell you: what is wrong with you, ... what tests are needed, ... what will happen to you, ... what treatment you need, ... and what you must do to help yourself. First, what is wrong

with you ...'. This technique can, of course, take up much time.

(3) The third method consists simply of *repeating* the most important bits of information.

(4) The fourth method consists of using *concrete* rather than *general* statements, for example 'You must be sure to weigh yourself once a week', instead of 'You must be sure you know how successful your diet is', or 'You need two full weeks holiday a year' instead of 'You must take proper holidays'.

All four methods individually have had some success in increasing recall. They have also been combined in a manual issued to some general practitioners, who found that this was effective in helping patients to remember more details of the consultation. It also appears that if patients remember more of the doctor's advice and instructions, they are more likely to show compliance, that is to co-operate with treatment.

Motivational processes

The cognitive explanations examined assume that the doctor and patient have identical goals, and that communication breaks down for what is essentially a technical reason. But Chapter 20 explains that patients may have a number of goals they wish to pursue, such as the development of a confiding relationship or permission to enter the sick role, which may not be explicit. Communication difficulties may arise because doctors do not recognise these other goals, or because these goals are in conflict with the doctor's wishes. Doctors often attempt to get patients to fit in to an established method or procedure of treatment which is convenient to medical staff, while patients may try to get these procedures altered to suit their own particular needs. This is especially likely to lead to conflict when resources such as time are in short supply. The doctor may be thinking of the roomful of people waiting to be seen, while the patient is trying to decide whether or not to broach some embarrassing or anxiety-laden subject.

Lack of recognition of patients' goals is also seen in the assumption made by some doctors that compliance is always the best thing for the patient. In some conditions, particularly chronic ones, patients have considerable knowledge of their disorders and may be better placed to make decisions than the doctor. Their decision not to take a particular drug, for instance, may be on very good grounds, a fact which could be obscured by labelling their behaviour as *non-compliant*. As discussed in Chapter 12, doctors seek *internalization* rather than simply compliance, and this can best be achieved by letting the patient enter into the decision-making process. Another example of conflict of goals arises when patients are diagnosed as having a terminal illness. Nobody likes to be the bearer of bad news, and doctors are no exception. Perhaps because of this 70–90% of doctors believe that patients should not be told they are dying, although 80–90% of patients claim that they would prefer to be told.

These motivational conflicts are sometimes inevitable, but can often be overcome if the doctor recognizes that the patient has a number of goals which may not have been made explicit. The doctor can encourage disclosure by improving *interviewing skills*, and being aware of *non-verbal* aspects of communication. Thus the doctor must appear to be relaxed and unhurried, and anxious to know the patient's point of view. The doctor must use appropriate eye-contact and not be simultaneously writing or reading medical notes. The distance between doctor and patient, whether physical or social, should be kept to a minimum and some rapport established with sociable, non-medical conversation. These are just a few of the interviewing skills which promote frank and full communication. Once doctors' and patients' goals are recognised and agreed, techniques can be used to make sure patients understand and remember the advice they are given. This should lead to high rates of patient satisfaction and compliance, with a consequent increase in doctor satisfaction.

Further reading:

Rachman S., ed. (1977) *Contributions to Medical Psychology*, Volume 1. Oxford, Pergamon. (See Chapter 2 by P. Ley.)
Tuckett D., ed. (1976) *An Introduction to Medical Sociology*. London, Tavistock. (See Chapter 6.)

CHAPTER 24

Provision of Services

Origins

Models of care, and the level to which provision is made, vary widely in different countries. In Britain the present organizational structure for the health service grew out of a war-time report (1942) of a committee headed by William Beveridge. The report envisaged: 'a comprehensive health and rehabilitation service for the prevention and cure of disease and restoration of capacity to work, available to all members of the community at the time of need'.

After much discussion and many attempts to accommodate the competing sets of interested parties, the 1946 *National Health Service Act* proposed a tripartite structure. Responsibility was to be shared between three statutory authorities: The Regional Hospital Boards, the Local Authorities, and the Local Executive Councils. The National Health Service (NHS) was born on the 5th of July, 1948, and its greatest achievement has been that benefits are available to all, free of charge, on the basis of need. Since the 1946 Act the NHS has been subject to two major reorganizations, in 1974 and 1982.

The National Health Service

At the head of the hierarchical structure of organization, as shown in Fig. 24.1, is the minister and his ministry: The Department of Health and Social Security. England is then divided into fourteen *Regional Health Authorities* (RHSs). Most of the members of a RHA are not professionally involved in the health service. They are unpaid, and appointed on a part-time basis by the ministry. This committee is augmented by *five* full-time managers who constitute

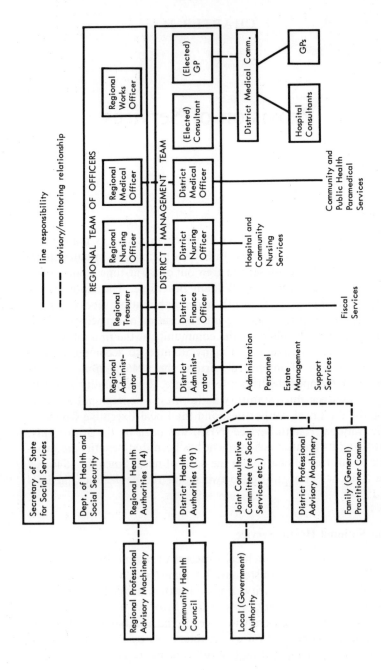

FIG. 24.1. Simplified organizational mode of the National Health Service.

the Regional team of officers.

The next level of organization is the *District Health Authority*, (DHA) numbering 191 in England. This too has a largely lay, part-time, unpaid committee, some of whose members may, however, be health professionals in their full-time occupation. A part-time paid chairperson is appointed by the Secretary of State. The DHA has four full-time chief officers who together with one consultant and one general practitioner, elected by their respective colleagues to serve on a part-time basis, constitute the *District Management Team* (DMT).

Each District is ideally responsible for providing integrated health care to about a quarter of a million people, although there is a wide variation in practice. The general practitioners are self-employed contractors to the NHS paid on a nationally agreed scale of capitation fees, item-for-service fees, and certain allowances. The contracts are held by a separate, locally based, *Family Practitioner Committee*. Meanwhile the *local authorities* are in control of social work, non-medical residential care and other community services. In order to facilitate the integration of services *Joint Consultative Committees* exist to plan collaboration between the hospital-based and local authority community-based services.

General practitioner services

About 50% of doctors who qualify enter general practice. Some 24 500 GPs provide a wide range of services to, on average, 2307 patients each. The trend, since 1948, has been away from the single-handed practitioner (18% in 1975). They have been replaced by group practices, some in purpose-built health centres (800 by 1975); 45% of practices have two or three doctors, whilst 37% have four or more.

In order to encourage a more equitable distribution of general practitioners the Secretary of State established a national Medical Practices Committee, the task of which is to assess the number of doctors practising in an area relative to population. These are assigned to one of four categories:

(1) designated area,
(2) open area,
(3) intermediate area, and
(4) restricted area.

Where the number of patients per doctor exceeds 2500, special encouragement to move into that area by means of a financial inducement is given (*designated area*). On the other hand, in a *restricted area*, where the average number of patients per doctor drops below 1800, entry is only allowed when a vacancy becomes available through death or retirement. An upper ceiling of 3500 patients for any single-handed doctor is also imposed. This may, at the discretion of the Family Practitioner Committee be raised by a further 2000 patients, if an assistant is recruited.

Community Health Councils

Community Health Councils (CHCs) were established, following the 1974 reorganization of the health service, with the task of representing the views of local users of the health services to the health authorities. It was an attempt to give the consumer a louder voice in planning and provision of services.

The councils range in size from eighteen to thirty-six members half of whom are nominated by the *local authorities*, one-third by *voluntary organizations*, and one-sixth by the *Regional Health Authority*. Usually two full-paid staff are appointed to the council, their salaries being paid by the RHA. Councils have varied in the way they interpret their brief, but they must examine the health care needs of the local population; examine existing services to see how they meet them; publicize the services offered, and give advice about how complaints may be made. They also tend to be consulted about future planning and intended changes which affect local health services.

In seeking to reflect the views and needs of the local community, CHCs have contributed to the shift in resources away from hospital to community services, and in the creation of a better balance of services within an area.

Cost

At its inception, some optimists anticipated that the new health service would actually decrease the number of cases, thereby keeping costs down. In fact the number of cases has continued to increase and the cost of both treatment and maintaining people, particularly the elderly, has increased enormously. In 1949 expenditure on the NHS was £450 million; by 1980 this figure had risen to £11 200 million. Even allowing for rising prices the NHS now costs three times as much as it did when it was established. However, the UK does not spend as much as many other developed countries on health services, even though as a proportion of gross national product the figure has risen from 3.9% in 1949 to 5.8% in 1980.

By far the largest part of the cost (87%) is born from direct taxation. The major portion of this money (63%) is spent upon the hospital-based services, compared with 6% on community health services and 11% on family practitioner services. 10% of expenditure is upon drugs.

Health services are expensive, largely because they are so labour intensive. About 1 in 20 of the total workforce are NHS employees. Nurses comprise nearly half of these as Table 24.1 makes clear.

TABLE 24.1.　NHS staff — U.K. (approximate figures 1979/80)

Staff	No.	Total (%)
Nursing and midwifery	430 000	43
Ancillary and others	219 700	22
Administrative and clerical	123 200	12
Doctors	67 200	7
Professional and technical	64 700	6
Works and maintenance	31 600	3
Pharmacists and opticians	27 800	3
Ambulance staff	20 900	2
Dentists	17 100	2
Total	1 003 000	100

TABLE 24.2.　Health and personal social services expenditure between different groups 1979/80

	%
General hospital and maternity	38.0
Primary care	19.7
Elderly people	14.3'
The mentally ill	7.5
Children	5.7
The mentally handicapped	4.3
Other	10.5
	100.0

This expenditure may also be looked at in another way, namely the particular client or patient groups to which it is directed. As Table 24.2 illustrates, general hospital and maternity patients absorb the greatest proportion of money.

Social services

Complimenting the health service are a number of what are generally termed *social services*. They too have been subject to reorganization, and may be seen as falling into three broad sectors.

(1) *Local authority social services departments* (Fig. 24.2)

Their work may be divided into four parts:
    (a) Residential services
        (i)   old people's accommodation (Part III homes),
        (ii) homes for the physically and mentally handicapped, and
        (iii) children: homes, reception centres, residential nurseries.
    (b) Field work services:
        (i)   child care: social work support and counselling to parents and children. Oversight of children at risk, particularly for non-accidental injury. Provision of services such as day nurseries and child minding,
        (ii) adoption, fostering, etc., and
        (iii) counselling, aids and advice to elderly, disabled and mentally ill.
    (c) Support services:
        (i)   day centres for elderly, physically and mentally disabled, etc.,
        (ii) home helps
        (iii) meals on wheels, and
        (iv) visiting warden services: particularly for the elderly.
    (d) Hospital services
        (i)   counselling patients and relatives,
        (ii) environmental assistance, particularly with regard to discharge, and adjusting to the return home,
        (iii) financial and practical help, and
        (iv) Liaison with other agencies to facilitate continuity of care.

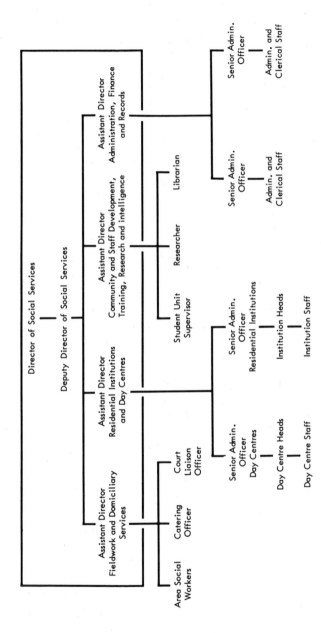

Fig. 24.2. Simplified organizational diagram of a typical social work department.

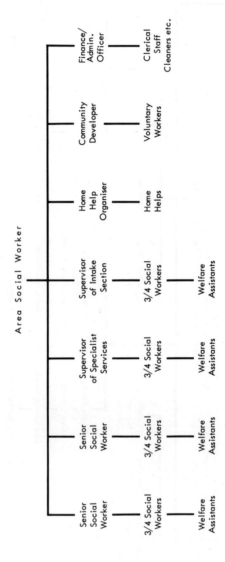

FIG. 24.3. Simplified organizational diagram of a local social work team.

Probation and after care services

This service is responsible to the Home Office, and is involved with a variety of largely court-based work. This includes: supervision of probation orders, preparing social enquiry reports for the court, prison after-care, parole orders, etc.

Voluntary agencies

In spite of the development of statutory services many voluntary agencies continue to flourish, often serving particular interest groups. In many cases they enable non-professionals to make a contribution to the care and well-being of others, and to provide a personalized service.

Local authority social services operate a system of care teams based upon smaller geographical areas in order to make both the workers, and the services they offer, more accesible to the community (Fig. 24.3).

Further reading:

Farmer R.D.T. & Miller D.L. (1983) *Lecture Notes on Epidemiology and Community Medicine*, 2nd Edition. Oxford, Blackwell Scientific Publications.

CHAPTER 25

Hospitalization

The stress of hospitalization

There are two main sources of stress associated with admission to hospital:

(1) Problems arising from illness, i.e. the stress attached to the illness itself and its implications.

(2) The hospital environment, i.e. the stress brought about by aspects of the hospital environment; for example, the admission procedure, staff behaviour and communication, the various investigatory and treatment procedures, achievement or otherwise of a satisfactory balance between privacy and companionship.

Obviously not all patients in hospital have the same kinds of experience. For a particular patient this depends on a number of factors, such as type of hospital, diagnosis and severity of the illness. The influence of the patient's personality and background is also important as it affects the way the patient behaves and the way they are perceived.

Patient and doctor roles

Patients may be regarded by staff as *good* or *bad* patients. Those who are *good* patients are usually submissive, undemanding and appreciative. *Bad* patients ask too many questions, refuse to do what they are told unless they are told why, demand more attention than the staff think they need and generally want a cooperative role. These extremes illustrate the opposite ends of a continuum of patient roles. The patient's perception of the doctor's role may also be characterised by a continuum, with an *omniscient* doctor at one extreme, and a doctor with *specific skills and knowledge* at the other.

Some patients seem to cope best with the stress of hospitalization when they regard their doctor as omniscient and adopt a state of total dependence. Others prefer to know what is happening to them. There are great individual differences but generally those with critical illnesses, at lower socioeconomic levels, or those who are very anxious favour the *omniscient doctor* and *submissive patient role*. Those not in a critical condition and at higher socioeconomic levels prefer a *cooperative patient role following the expert advice of a specialist*. It has been observed that some patients shift their preferences during their hospital stay, for example as they feel themselves getting better or worse. This tendency to shift from one role to another and the recognition of differences in individual needs illustrates the usefulness of viewing both the doctors' and patients' roles in terms of flexible continua along which both may move.

Emotional reactions to hospitalization

Adverse emotion can complicate the course of recovery from illness, reduce the effectiveness of treatment, and even cause illness. Given that any person is emotionally vulnerable when under the impact of illness and hospitalization, responsible care of patients must recognise emotional reactions and deal with them appropriately.

There are at least four kinds of emotion, or manifestations of distress that are commonly encountered, either singly or in combination:

(1) anxiety/fear,
(2) depression,
(3) irritability/anger, and
(4) dependence/submissiveness

(1) *Anxiety/fear*

Patients newly arrived in hospital are frequently in a state of extreme anxiety. A study of patient anxiety on admission to hospital found that patients on four general wards were significantly more anxious than the general population outside hospital, and one-fifth of those questioned were more anxious than most patients attending a psychiatric clinic. This anxiety and fear may be expressed verbally in direct statements, or by repeatedly asking the same questions, or in the intolerant demanding of attention or making pleas for reassurance. Alternatively the person may say nothing and 'withdraw into themselves'. Anxiety may then demonstrate itself in physiological distress, for example, pallor, restlessness, sweating, muscular tension, stomach upsets, diarrhoea or constipation.

Intense feelings of anxiety and fear may interfere with the efficiency of treatment and prolong the recovery process. For example, Klopfer studied differences between patients with fast-growing cancers and those with slowly developing ones. He found that those with faster growing cancers were more anxious.

(2) *Depression*

Depression is the second most frequently reported adverse reaction to disease and its treatment. It is important to distinguish between the depression that is a reaction to disease and hospitalization, and that which is more long-standing in the patient's history. Depression occurring in response to hospitalization usually has a relatively sudden onset. There is a generalised slowing down of bodily and thought processes, reduction in interests, feeling of sadness and an unwillingness to talk, inability to eat adequately or to become involved in activity. Unlike more long-standing depression, self-control is usually maintained and there is enough energy for brief periods of normal mood.

(3) *Anger*

Anger is a common reaction to the frustration of being incapacitated. It is particularly important because it can cause problems in interpersonal relations and so affect patient management. Anger or irritability should be treated by staff as a reaction to the patient's condition and not a reason for accusing the patient of ingratitude or uncooperativeness.

(4) *Dependence/submissiveness*

Dependence is a further form of emotional expression which may accompany physical illness and complicate treatment. During illness a patient may *regress* and behave in ways more appropriate to an earlier stage of development by becoming selfish, demanding immediate attention, and refusing to help themself. Total dependency may be appropriate during serious illness, but with improvement the patient needs to be helped towards the reinstatement of independence.

Children in hospital

For a child, going into hospital is a major event. It has been estimated that by 7 years of age 45% of children have been admitted to hospital at least once (one-third for tonsillectomy). While this proportion is now considerably less in some parts of the country, it still remains numerically large.

Younger children (usually under 4 years of age), anxious children, and those already coping with a considerable amount of stress in their lives are the most likely to experience considerable distress. This is ameliorated by the increasing provision for a parent, or another familiar person, to visit them for much of the day or to stay in hospital with the child. These provisions (in the UK) have largely grown from the Platt committee recommendations in 1959, which investigated problems relating to children in hospital. Three of their recommendations have been particularly important and far-reaching in helping hospitals meet the needs of children:

(1) unrestricted visits by parents,

(2) the establishment of mother–child units, and

(3) the admission of children only when absolutely necessary.

These recommendations have been widely accepted, although not universally implemented. In 1970 three further recommendations were added:

(4) occupation should be provided for the children: there should be a diverse programme of ward activities, play, recreation and school,

(5) the removal of physical and professional barriers to parental visiting, with the staff encouraging and actively helping parents to contribute positively to the care of their child,

(6) improved preparation for admission to hospital and health education both for children and their parents.

Conclusion

Hospitalization presents a major stress to most people of all ages. Exactly how this stress is manifest varies with the individual, type and severity of the illness. Some studies have shown that appropriate preparation, both for admission to hospital and for specific procedures, may result in decreased need for analgesics, faster recovery times, earlier discharge and more successful long-term adjustment.

Further reading:

Rachman S.J. & Philips C. (1978) *Psychology and Medicine*, Harmondsworth, Penguin, (Chapter 11).
Tuckett D. & Kaufert J.M. (Eds) (1979) *Medical Sociology*. London, Tavistock, (Chapter 21).

CHAPTER 26

Psychological and Social Aspects of Physical Illness

When the body is in a state of health, its organs and functions are in dynamic equilibrium. Amongst their other functions the various systems of the body maintain the metabolism of the brain and thereby allow it to perform its motor, sensory, cognitive and emotional tasks. Any disturbance of the major systems of the body can change brain function, and through it, behaviour. The human organism is also in a state of dynamic equilibrium with its environment. Changes in the environment and changes in the relationship between the environment and the organism are conveyed to the organism through the various functions of the nervous system. In its turn the nervous system, largely through its autonomic and endocrine connections, can influence the functioning of many organs in the body.

Events both within and without the body can influence each other through the nervous system. Probably the best-known example of this mechanism is the preparation for *flight or fight* as described by the physiologist, Cannon, in the early part of this century. An animal perceiving a danger is physiologically prepared for physical effort to enable it to escape, by the secretion of adrenaline by the suprarenal glands and by the action of the sympathetic nervous system. Twenty-five years later the physiologist, Selye, described mechanisms whereby the body prepares and sustains responses to various kinds of stressing experiences which may be either physical, as in a surgical operation, or psychological, as in prolonged periods of anxiety. The mechanisms of Selye's *general adaptation syndrome* (GAS) are discussed in Chapter 17.

Mechanisms of this kind mean that physical and psychological functions of the body are inextricably interrelated. As a result scarcely any physical illness does not have its psychological effects, nor any psychological illness or event its physical manifestations. In most cases of physical illness the psychological aspects do not require special attention, but in some cases important psychological complications arise which may influence the course of the illness or occasionally come to dominate the clinical picture.

Individual patients vary in the way they respond to both physical illness and emotional distress. Such variation arises from the personality of the patient, his previous experience of illness, the nature of the current illness, and the way in which the case is managed by the doctor. All doctors need to appreciate the ways in which emotional factors may influence the course of physical illness, and to utilise such factors in treating illness effectively, as well as in dealing with patients and their relatives satisfactorily.

Common problems in management

The importance of the management of ill patients including emphasis upon psychological and social factors, is best seen from examples of problems which commonly arise. In acute physical illness a patient may experience an abrupt change from being completely well to having his life threatened by his condition. Great uncertainty may surround his future life and even survival. Both patient and relatives are helped by discussing with the doctor the progress of investigation and treatment of illness. Reassurance may be helpful when it is realistic and makes proper allowances for uncertainties which are present. A lack of communication with the patient and his family can give rise to great distress and affect recovery from illness or from surgical operation.

Pain is a common symptom of ill health (Chapter 15). Psychological factors can greatly alter a patient's ability to tolerate a painful illness and markedly influence the effects of analgesics and other pain-relieving measures.

Disabling illnesses alter the life-styles of subjects and demand radical changes in the patient's hopes and potential. This adjustment may be particularly difficult when a patient has taken pride and pleasure in an activity which is no longer possible.

Sometimes illnesses leave a patient deformed or otherwise changed in appearance; for instance, following certain operations and road traffic accidents. Apart from functional disabilities arising from deformities a patient may feel self-conscious and have difficulty in meeting old friends and appearing in public places. Deformities are particularly important if they reduce sexual attractiveness and a patient's confidence in sexual relationships.

Terminal illnesses require special consideration (Chapter 27). Most patients in these circumstances not only experience concern over the effects of the illness on themselves, but also the effects on their relatives. There is often concern as well for their affairs to be put in order. Medical management of the illness may become, even from the patient's point of view, a secondary matter.

Social effects of physical illness

Illness may change a person's life suddenly and permanently and lead to social consequences that are difficult to deal with. This may totally alter the patient's relationship with his or her spouse. Perhaps the spouse is now expected to undertake onerous tasks in the patient's care, take responsibility for the household, or become the main breadwinner. Their sexual relationship may be seriously impaired. Relationships with children may also be altered depending upon the ages of parent and child. Patients with younger children or grandchildren may be prevented from joining in activities with the children which they had previously enjoyed. Alternatively the patient's illness may make demands upon the children that they may be unable to meet, or to fulfil only with difficulty. In the case of middle-aged children of patients, a conflict may arise between the needs of their sick parents and of their own children. The illness of a young person is both a source of great distress to parents and also a considerable practical and emotional burden upon them.

Patients often have to be absent from work during periods of acute illness, and chronic illness may force a change of job or even premature retirement. For many patients work has been a great source of interest and satisfaction in earlier life. Loss of employment is often difficult for a patient to accept, involving as it does loss of status and earnings. Social activities may decline through loss of contacts at work, decreasing mobility and a loss of income.

Reactions to illness

Most illnesses occasion some distress, but this is recognised as being in keeping with the illness both in form and in severity. This understandable reaction is sometimes referred to as *dysphoria*. Less frequently patients show emotional reactions which are severe in degree and require attention in their own right. These emotional states are sometimes reactions to an illness and its effects, and sometimes a concomitant effect of the illness itself. These important reactions have been described in Chapter 25 in the context of hospitalization.

Physical illnesses can affect the brain itself in two ways:

(1) by altering the bodily equilibrium and thereby changing the brain's internal environment and altering its functions, or

(2) by directly involving the brain in a morbid process which leads to the destruction of brain tissue and a permanent change in brain function.

The first type of condition is usually temporary and is caused by the accompaniments of physical illness such as pyrexia, dehydration, acute respiratory, cardiac or renal failure, intoxication by drugs and a wide range of similar factors. The clinical syndromes seen are known as *toxic confusional states* and are characterized by: a change in consciousness or *delirium, disorientation* in time and place, frighteningly vivid visual *hallucinations, restlessness* and anxiety, *suspiciousness*, and a marked *fluctuation* of symptoms which follow the progress of the toxic state. These conditions carry the same prognosis as the underlying cause, nowadays the appearance of mental symptoms is not necessarily a sinister development.

Disorders that lead to the permanent loss of brain tissue are associated with a gradual but irreversible impairment of intellectual function. Clinically, consciousness is unimpaired but there is disorientation and a loss of concentration, impairment of memory especially for recent events, loss of interest and drive, and occasionally difficulty in speech and complex motor activities. These conditions are often progressive and lead to severe dementia. Causes include degenerative, infective and neoplastic diseases.

The development of a psychiatric illness in patients already physically ill may lead to the psychiatric problems dominating the clinical picture and gaining precedence in management. In other circumstances the treatment of physical illness may be seriously impeded by disturbed behaviour, lack of co-operation, and difficulties in communication. Occasionally the patient's behaviour may be life-threatening, in preventing essential treatment.

Further reading:

Cannon W.B. (1915) *Bodily Changes in Pain, Hunger, Fear and Rage.* New York, D. Appleton & Co.

Cohn K.A. (1982) Chemotherapy from an insider's perspective. *Lancet* i 1006–1009.

Selye H. (1950) *The Physiology and Pathology of Exposure to Stress,* Montreal, Acta Inc.

CHAPTER 27

Bereavement and Terminal Illness

Terminal care

As life expectancy increases more people are faced with the prospect of chronic ill health. Fear of death from a known disease process is an understandable but very stressful experience. Certain diagnoses carry the implication of inexorable deterioration, for example cancer, although the prognosis is not necessarily bad (one out of three patients in whom cancer is diagnosed may be expected to recover). Other illnesses may have just as chronic and potentially fatal an outcome, and yet the future is regarded with less dread. The psychological consequences of terminal illness have become better understood in recent years, and the care of many individual patients can be greatly improved by knowledge of the stages involved.

In order to come to terms with serious and potentially terminal illness the patient must know something about his condition and its seriousness. It is part of the doctor's task to give patients 'bad news' about their health, but they find this very difficult. Much of the difficulty arises from a wish to spare the patient added pain, but other considerations include an inability to cope with the patient's distress, feelings of failure, and an understandable wish on the doctor's part to avoid sharing the patient's suffering. Few doctors have been taught how to impart bad news, and yet the majority of those patients who are dying know what is happening to them from non-verbal cues even though those looking after them say nothing. Hardest to bear is the situation where the family are advised not to tell the prognosis to the patient. The patient, dimly or even fully aware of his situation, is denied the chance to talk about his feelings and his future with those close to him. He tries to spare the family any pain, believing that they are in ignorace.

162

Most patients and their families, given the opportunity to ask questions, want as much information as they can cope with emotionally. Such a seeking of information by the patient should be a dialogue, so that the sensitive doctor not only answers questions but tries to find out what prompted them, what the patient has noticed, and what is feared. Misunderstandings can be corrected, the truth given and accepted gradually, and bald statements suggesting a terrifying future avoided.

An immediate reaction to bad news of any sort is often numbness and *denial*. Knowledge that a person is terminally ill is no exception; the patient and relatives may be under the impression that they have been told nothing, when the doctor believes he has been quite explicit. This may extend to a *search* for a second opinion, hopefully more favourable, or to the seeking of hazardous or unproven treatments. Temporary periods of denial remain part of coping during the whole of the course of a terminal illness; it is very difficult to stare death in the face all the time. Once the numbness and denial have diminished a little, the patient may well become *angry* at his fate, feeling it is undeserved, and express this anger in hostility and awkwardness towards those close to him, both family and those professionally involved. Patients with a strong religious faith may feel a distressing and frightening anger towards God. Many will, for a time, bargain with God in their minds, promising to live blameless lives in the future if granted a reprieve. Gradually awareness of the inevitability of death develops and an appropriate and often profound *sadness* follows which leads finally to *acceptance*. Out of this solution *hope* develops, if not for the future after death, at least for the more immediate enjoyment of the company of family and friends, of talking over past pleasures, and of making plans for those who remain (making a will can sometimes be therapeutic). Separation, of an emotional kind, or *detachment* from others sometimes occurs shortly before death.

The availability of *information*, honestly given when requested, and the absence of barriers to the expression of feelings with relatives, help an individual to cope with terminal illness. Consistent support for both the patient and family are essential prerequisites for good medical care.

Symptom relief, particularly the correct use of analgesics, allows many dying patients to remain at home. For those without families or who need intensive medical and nursing treatment, hospice or hospital care may be necessary, either to gain control of symptoms or to give families a rest. The aims here are care and comfort, not 'cure'. Families often want to be together when a member is dying, and may well find grieving easier when this is possible. Shared knowledge may allow the survivors to grieve with the dying person, and this makes a painful time easier for both.

Recently developed treatments, for instance some of the chemo-therapeutic agents, sometimes produce a miraculous but often temporary improvement in patients with terminal illness, and families may grieve in anticipation of death at each exacerbation. Apparent but short-term recovery may leave them unable to re-commit themselves emotionally to the sick person, with consider-able distress on both sides.

Bereavement

Just as there seems to be a pattern of response to the knowledge of impending death, so the experience of bereavement involves a process of stages of emotional adjustment. Bereavement is usually taken to indicate the loss, by death, of a loved person, but the experience of other losses such as loss of a limb by amputation, of a person by divorce, of a pet, of job or status, of loved material possessions, and of physical fitness may involve a similar adjust-ment.

The immediate reaction is often *numbness, shock* and *disbelief*. The bereaved individual cannot accept the fact of loss, and may carry on as though nothing had happened, coping well at a practi-cal level whilst being unable to react emotionally. This is followed hours or days later by a period of *acute grief* during which the individual experiences great distress and longing, often in pangs of almost unbearable intensity. He feels frightened, restless yet barely able to do anything, may go looking for the lost person and may have great difficulty sleeping. He may feel the dead person's pre-sence, hear their voice, or even see the person. He may reproach himself for imagined neglect of the dead person, and may project his anger at being left alone onto family, friends, professionals, and sometimes God. This very painful period usually lasts days or weeks, gradually becoming a less intense but nonetheless *profound sadness* which may last several weeks, months or even a year or more, slowly lifting as a new way of life is developed. Resurgence of grief at anniversaries of the death and other evocative times of year often occur with an intensity which surprises the bereaved person.

The bereaved can be helped in a number of ways, all of which acknowledge the loss. This, of course, runs counter to the current 'Anglo-Saxon' practice of getting everything over quickly 'without any fuss', so that there can be a pretence that nothing has happened. Practical help with arrangements for the funeral and with caring for the bereaved family are most important initially. People need time to grieve and they should be allowed or allow themselves to express their grief in tears, in talking and in dignified religious observances. A grave to visit is helpful for many people as it legitimizes grief at a specific place. Similarly, regular visits from friends after the funeral are beneficial, and they should be prepared to talk about the dead person. Too rapid clearing out of the deceased's possessions, or change of house, is to be discouraged. Major decisions made at this time may well work out badly. Once the intensity of grief begins to diminish, gentle encouragement to take up previous interests, or to undertake new ones may be helpful. However, new relationships and radical changes of life are best avoided for many months until the acute grief has been resolved.

The intensity of grief varies with the nature of the previous relationship and the severity of the loss. Sudden death, the death of children, and deaths where relationships have been markedly ambivalent often cause the most prolonged suffering. What is clear is that grief is unavoidable. If it is inhibited, so that the individual carries on as though nothing had happened, then a later loss, even a trivial one, may result in very intense grief, or the individual may later develop a depressive illness. In some of the bereaved, grief is never resolved but remains disabling for months or even years. Such people need skilled help.

As a stress, bereavement may also be reflected in physical symptoms. Bereaved people suffer worse physical ill health in the year after their loss, with an increase in consultations for minor symptoms and an increase in serious morbidity, especially heart disease, compared with a matched population who had not been bereaved. Attention to the psychological aspects of bereavement may not only bring some comfort in the early stages but may also make the difference between future ill-health and well being. Help after bereavement (and also while it is being prepared for) is an important part of preventive medicine. Much of this is carried out by friends and relatives, but the doctor who is aware of the problems and also what is possible in mitigation, is able to aid the bereaved person and also to advise people close to such a person.

Further reading:

Parkes C.M. (1978) *Bereavement: Studies of Grief in Adult Life.* Harmondsworth, Penguin.
Kubler-Ross E. (1970) *On Death and Dying.* London, Tavistock.

CHAPTER 28

Handicap

The concept of handicap originated in the world of horseracing. It implied an extra weight or other condition imposed to equalize the chances of runners. However, in current usage a handicap might be taken to mean 'anything that makes life harder' for an individual. The consequences of some accidents and physical illnesses are often handicapping, but intellectual impairments, and those resulting from mental illness and from environmental and social causes have also to be considered.

Primary handicap

These are handicaps resulting directly from genetic endowment, accident or illness and would include the limited intellectual capacity of mental handicap, loss of limbs or function resulting from accident or physical illness, and the more intangible but often devastating loss of social capacity that results from mental illness.

Primary handicap may be static and therefore predictable, or may diminish slowly as coping mechanisms are developed. When disability is part of chronic ill-health, there may be the implication of gradual deterioration over months or years, or the threat of sudden exacerbation. Primary handicap is more often single in younger people (for instance an amputated leg), and multiple in the elderly (physical illness and impaired cognitive function, together with emotional and social disabilities).

Secondary handicap

Whether handicaps are single or multiple, static or progressive, those suffering them and their circumstances are always in a state of change or adaptation. Secondary handicaps are the adverse consequences of the primary handicap rather than of the original underlying condition, and may involve all aspects of the individual's life. Personal reactions include grief for lost capabilities, feelings of bitterness and increased dependence upon others. Whereas acceptance of this dependence may be necessary for the severely disabled, overdependence may limit the use of remaining resources. Self-esteem flags and feelings of worthlessness may lead to a withdrawal from other people, and a lack of involvement in life.

Handicap may have deleterious effects upon the whole family; an individual, for example a handicapped child, may be rejected by one parent and consequent conflict may even break up the family. Other family members may feel that attention is lavished upon the disabled individual whilst they are being neglected. Such a person living at home may be well supported, or even overprotected, but families may have reached equilibrium only after a profoundly disturbing time. Caring for a disabled person may impoverish the fit members of the family both financially and socially. Members of the community at large may not know how to treat a handicapped person; they may react with fear and avoidance making the sufferer's isolation worse.

The most severely handicapped, irrespective of cause, are cared for in institutions which are task-orientated, instead of person-orientated. Such a mode of care adds considerably to other handicaps because it cuts the individual off from the outside world and from close personal contacts. It limits or removes important choices in life leading to apathy, lack of initiative, loss of interest in the world outside, submissiveness and resigned acceptance. Change is resisted and a loss of individuality occurs. Even in the community similar changes may occur because of isolation and lack of choice or variety in life. Such effects of secondary handicap are cumulative and self-perpetuating.

The more developed an individual's psychological and social skills are, and the more favourable his material circumstances, the better equipped he is to compensate for a handicapping condition. Low intelligence, not amounting to mental handicap, makes life difficult. Poverty and social deprivation are hard to cope with even if the individual is healthy. Those with difficult personalities find the acceptance of handicap particularly hard and have problems co-operating with those who help them. Other physical handicaps, for instance blindness, deafness, and epilepsy, may make an individual very vulnerable to further, even minor, impairment. A lack of close relationships and of family support also hinder coping. Some of these attributes, particularly lack of family ties and interests, a lack of motivation and a dislike of social interactions, along with poverty and increasing age, make individuals more likely to be admitted to institutions and more likely, once there, to become very dependent upon them and thus reluctant to leave.

Rehabilitation

Ideally, the handicapped person should be helped to live the fullest and most independent life possible within the true limits of his disability. Rehabilitation programmes need to concentrate upon the strengths that individuals retain and to maximize support from families and friends. Information should be given as early as possible to the handicapped person and those concerned with his care, about prospects, likely emotional reactions, services available and possible helping agencies. The development of practical skills and alterations to the physical environment are important, but the attitudes and reactions of those around him, the social environment, may be more so. The handicapped individual needs to achieve a balance between accepting help and on occasions taking such risks as are necessary to prevent overdependence.

Changes in the philosophy of care have taken place in recent years with the realization that the handicapped are able to live fuller lives in the community than in institutions. They should, wherever possible, both have their own homes and care for themselves. Co-operation between the many different groups providing help is necessary and new professional roles are required. Health visitors and social workers often are trained to care for the young but find the elderly most in need of their expertise. Doctors and nurses are trained to 'cure', but find much of their work involves caring for the chronically ill of all ages, particularly the elderly.

Size of the handicapped population

Accurate figures are very difficult to come by. Some handicaps are obvious and easy to identify; others are hidden, especially those due to psychiatric illness.

Physical handicap

In 1971 a sample survey was carried out of the population over 16 years of age living in private households in the United Kingdom. The results indicated that there were at least:

150 000 very severely handicapped people needing special care,

356 000 severely handicapped people needing considerable support,

616 000 appreciably handicapped people needing some support, and

approximately 2 million people physically impaired but needing little support for everyday living activities.

Nearly 60% of the impaired were elderly; the most common single cause was arthritis.

This survey also indicated that a high proportion of the handicapped were not on local authority registers of substantially or permanently handicapped persons. Approximately one-half of the disabled population, and two-thirds of those with appreciable handicaps, had no regular help from local services.

Mental handicap

Three per cent of the population have an intelligence quotient (IQ) below 70 (the level of intelligence currently accepted as the dividing line, although IQ is not the sole criterion of mental handicap). Approximately 3 per 1000 of the population have an IQ below 50 indicating severe subnormality of intelligence.

Mental illness as a cause of handicap

There are no comprehensive figures for handicap caused by mental illness. Perhaps the most useful figure is that during each year about 14% of the population have psychological symptoms of sufficient severity to disturb their life and require help from the general practitioner.

Provisions for the handicapped

There is no unified system of provision for the handicapped, who have a wide variety of needs. Care is not well co-ordinated and this adds to the difficulty of encouraging the handicapped to make their own decisions.

Health services

Through general practitioner services and hospital facilities the following are offered:

(1) Diagnostic services, treatment of diseases, and assessment of primary handicap.

(2) Provision of rehabilitation services for both physical and psychological disabilities.

(3) Provision of residential care for some groups of the most severely handicapped (the mentally handicapped, the mentally ill, young and old chronic sick, elderly severely mentally infirm).

Local authority services

People living at home have very varied needs. Increasing emphasis is being placed on care in non-residential settings and as a result (in the UK) of the *Chronically Sick and Disabled Persons Act* (1970), many local authority functions are mandatory. They include collecting data on the numbers and needs of substantially and permanently handicapped persons, including the mentally handicapped, and informing those who might benefit from the help available to them. Local authorities are also responsible for the provision of help in the home (such as home helps, housing alterations, items of equipment and so on); for recreational and educational facilities with appropriate transport; for residential provision (from adapted normal housing to premises for residential care); for special car parking facilities, and for access to public buildings with adequate sanitary facilities. Good liaison between health and social services is always necessary but often difficult to achieve.

Department of Health and Social Security

The DHSS provides basic financial assistance to handicapped people who are unable to work, according to need. The Supplementary Benefits Commission provides extra allowances for special diets, for fuel and for clothing. Other benefits include Industrial

Injuries Benefit, the Constant Attendance Allowance for people who require long-term help from relatives, neighbours, or other carers and the Mobility Allowance.

Manpower Services Commission

Disablement Resettlement Officers help those handicapped who are capable of returning to work, by offering gradual readjustment to working situations at the Employment Resettlement Centres, and training schemes at Skills Centres for those who need to take up new work. The whole scheme inevitably becomes less effective in times of high unemployment.

Voluntary organizations

There are many organizations involved in providing help for the handicapped. It is easier for them, rather than the statutory bodies, to experiment with new ideas on a small scale. They often provide money for research and can act as pressure groups in the interest of the handicapped. A disadvantage is that they may be more likely to help those easier to rehabilitate, and may leave the more severely disabled and the more disagreable to statutory bodies.

Further reading:

Wing J.K. & Morris B. (1981) *Handbook of Psychiatric Rehabilitation Practice*. Oxford, Oxford University Press.

CHAPTER 29

Health Education

Health education

Some of the more significant improvements in health have come about, not by advances in medicine as such, but by changes in the behaviour of members of the population. Simple procedures such as washing hands and cleaning teeth are important in the prevention of illness, but as with all human behaviour, these habits must initially be learned. People have to be taught the value of these behaviours, the process of education being formal or informal. Advances in the understanding of illness often lead to the development of preventive procedures, but these are not effective unless they are communicated and taught efficiently to those at risk. Despite the fact that prevention has proved more effective than treatment in improving health nationally, doctors are less concerned with helping their patients avoid illness, than with treating them when they have become ill. We are far from being able to prevent all illness, but there are some conditions where prevention is possible. In Chapter 18 a number of instances where illness is clearly related to the behaviour of the individual were described. This chapter considers some of the issues in the modification of behaviour with the goal of preventing illness.

Health education has two aspects: *information*, and *modification*. Information provides people with facts relevant to the development of illness, and modification teaches them to do something about it. Most health education to date has concentrated on the dissemination of information; the modification aspects being mostly restricted to pious exhortations to stop smoking, stop eating too much and start jogging. Adequate instructions on achieving these ends are rarely given. Information per se does not necessarily

173

lead to a change in behaviour. Patients often say they are aware of the links between smoking and cancer, drinking and brain damage, or cream buns and coronaries, but they cannot stop smoking, drinking or eating to excess, even though they try. It has already been pointed out in Chapter 18 that behaviour is not always rational, and as a consequence, self-control is not always as easy as it might at first appear, particularly to the doctor.

Applications of health education

Two main applications of health education may be identified. The first is education directed towards *prevention*. This includes both the establishment of healthy behaviour patterns such as washing hands after visiting the toilet, brushing teeth after every meal, taking exercise and having children immunised; and the avoidance of potentially harmful behaviours such as smoking excessively or using dangerous drugs. The second application refers to techniques of *modification* where the 'bad' behaviour patterns are already established and the first signs of illness may have appeared. In this group education is directed at heavy smokers, the obese and the overstressed.

Any form of education has as its prime aim, the establishment of permanent changes within the individual. These do not, of course, occur unless the individual is motivated to change, that is the learner agrees with the statements of the educator and wishes to change. In the present context, this process is related to the assessment of risk involved in certain behaviours as mentioned in Chapter 18. For example, the committed smoker may deny the validity of the relationship between smoking and cancer; or he may accept it in general, but deny its relevance to his particular case. What happens here is that, when faced with information which suggests that he is, in fact, behaving foolishly or dangerously, he tends to deny, distort, invalidate or otherwise ignore the evidence. This is an area of social psychology known as *cognitive dissonance* and is important and relevant where attitudes are to be changed or influenced in some way, as in advertising or in politics. If I deny that smoking is harmful, I do not perceive it as risky, and I can therefore happily continue. I have to be persuaded otherwise before I will co-operate with any education programme. If I believe that vaccination is harmful, I will not expose my children to what I see as a risk. I have to be persuaded otherwise before I will change my behaviour.

Persuasion and attitude change

Persuasion in this context requires more than the provision of information. The good educator has to enquire why *wrong* beliefs are held before they can be changed. This takes us back to Chapter 18. Beliefs and attitudes are as much a part of *behaviour* as are overt motor acts, and are subject to the same laws of learning and maintainance. Attitudes are held because they are rewarded, and efficient education must incorporate the assessment of the relevant rewards.

The whole area of attitude change is rather poorly researched at present, but is clearly relevant to health education. It would seem, from what evidence is available, that the more effective techniques for attitude change involve the use of group influences together with identifiable authoritative figures providing both information and good models. Thus, methods to reduce smoking in teenagers using group discussions with young people and the views of important figures such as sport or pop stars who do not smoke, are likely to be more effective than a series of lectures given by a man in a white coat, even if he is presented as a highly respected chest physician. Doctors are more likely to believe information read in the *British Medical Journal* than in the *Reader's Digest*. Alcoholics Anonymous uses ex-alcoholics rather than health professionals to achieve its aim. *Self-help* groups are probably effective, not because of inadequacies in medical care or expertise, but simply because the members of such groups, be they alcoholics, phobics or gamblers, are seen as more *authoritative* than any health professional, unless this person is or has been, an alcoholic, a phobic or a gambler.

The effectiveness of information is also a function of a number of other variables, particularly those to do with the physical presentation of the material. If it is in the form of a leaflet, a presentation in the style of the *Daily Mirror* (or any other mass circulation paper) is understood by more people than one written in the style of the *Times* (or other 'upmarket' publication). Short words, short sentences and larger print are more comprehensible and therefore better remembered by most people. Because of their relative sophistication with language, doctors are not necessarily the best communicators, although they may be perceived as being more knowledgeable.

Educating people by giving information is thus not just a simple matter of telling them what to do. They must be prepared to accept what is said, they must comprehend it and they must act upon it. This depends as much upon who is giving the information and the manner of its presentation as on the information itself. The good health educator must have the ability to sell a refrigerator to an Eskimo.

Behavioural modification

Persuading someone to change their behaviour, in the sense of not doing something that is already part of their behavioural repertoire, is probably more difficult. We have seen that established behaviour is maintained by complex patterns of reinforcement. This reinforcement must be understood before change can occur. Understanding is best achieved by a detailed analysis of the behaviours, with particular respect to the antecedents and consequences in terms of thoughts, feelings, actions and stimuli. Thus, if I see a cream bun and think, 'One won't do any harm', I am more likely to eat it than if I say to myself, 'One is one too many'. Obese people eat more when food is freely available than those of average weight. Restricting the amount of food available controls the eating; that is, controlling the discriminative stimuli controls the behaviour. A good additional strategy is to substitute alternative behaviours which are incompatible with the target behaviours. Thus, visiting the library is incompatible with drinking in the bar, and doing forty press-ups prevents you from making a sandwich for yourself.

If a new behaviour is to become established, it too must be rewarded, preferably immediately. In this context, the support of others, that is social reinforcement, is vital. A slimmer in a roomful of fatties is almost bound to fail. Again, the use of group influences is important, together with some concrete evidence of success, such as a daily record of cigarettes not smoked, or a weekly record of weight lost or of money saved. It is, however, important to realise that the conditions for learning are different for each individual, and the modification programme for each person is different, although the principles alluded to above are quite general.

One currently popular application of these principles is in *stress management*, with particular emphasis on the self-control of emotional or, psychosomatic disorders such as anxiety and hypertension, without the use of drugs. The basic techniques require the individual to be able to recognise whether the way in which they are responding to an environmental event is potentially harmful or not. Once a *stress response* is identified then methods for reducing it can be employed. The self-control variants of relaxation mentioned in Chapter 10 are popular at present, although their long-term effectiveness has yet to be evaluated. Thus, the effect of a stressful stimulus may be deliberately limited, both in magnitude and in duration. An alternative approach is to identify those situations likely to be perceived as stressful, and either to avoid them or to modify one's perception of them. Avoidance is not always appropriate, so some form of *cognitive restructuring* is usually called for. Instead of getting angry at a consultant when he criticises you unfairly, you could say to yourself 'perhaps he is on edge because he was called away in the middle of a golf match'.

Health education is a complex activity. It requires an understanding of human behaviour and an appreciation that there is more to learning than just receiving information. All treatment is, in a sense, health education, and all doctors are teachers. The principles of learning are thus just as important to doctors as those of physiology and biochemistry.

Index